C000016645

Miscellaneous Philosophy

The Underclassman Years

Stefan Koski

Miscellaneous Philosophy: The Underclassman Years

Copyright © 2005 Stefan Koski. All rights reserved. No part of this book may be reproduced or retransmitted in any form or by any means without the written permission of the publisher.

Published by Hats Off Books®
610 East Delano Street, Suite 104
Tucson, Arizona 85705 U.S.A.
www.hatsoffbooks.com

International Standard Book Number: 1-58736-411-5
Library of Congress Control Number: 2004115625

The quote after the section "Sixteen Years in the Life" was excerpted from *How Rude! The Teenagers' Guide to Good Manners, Proper Behavior, and Not Grossing People Out* by Alex J. Packer, PhD (©1997); used with permission from Free Spirit Publishing Inc., Minneapolis, Minnesota; (800) 735-7323; www.freespiritpublishing.com; all rights reserved.

DEDICATED TO

Liana, who gave me the best childhood memories that I could ever ask for,

and Rachel, who guided me through my freshman year (and continues to guide me) with the utmost of realism.

If it wasn't for you two, I would have been gone long ago.

*My entire philosophy is that
somewhere,
at some point,
I missed something.
And it was important.*
        —*Stefan Koski*

ACKNOWLEDGEMENTS

Quotes from Dale Carnegie, Elbert Hubbard, Robert Heinlein, Edward Abbey, R. A. Dickson, Hunter S. Thompson, P. J. O'Rourke, Cicero, Albert Einstein, C. S. Lewis, Tom Peters, The First Law of Applied Terror, Henry Brooks Adams, Ambrose Bierce, Napoleon Bonaparte, Karl Marx, David Harold Fink, Peter Burke, Kahlil Gibran, Winston Churchill, George Orwell, Abigail Van Buren, John Masefield, Ronald Reagan, *The Rule of Failure*, Fran Liebowitz, Conway's Law, G. H. Hardy, Peter Griffin, Charles Kettering, Jane Wagner, Lane Kirkland, Katherine Mansfield, Finley Peter Dunn, Bill Cosby, and Alex J. Packer, PhD.

The quote after the section "Holy Sh*t...I Just Realized How Much I Hate Math" was taken from Peter Griffin, from the television show *Family Guy* (created by Seth MacFarlane). The episode in question was "When You Wish Upon a Weinstein," written by Ricky Blitt and directed by Dan Povenmire (©2003 Twentieth Century Fox).

The quote after the section "Sixteen Years in the Life" was excerpted from *How Rude! The Teenagers' Guide to Good Manners, Proper Behavior, and Not Grossing People Out* by Alex J. Packer, PhD (©1997); used with permission from Free Spirit Publishing Inc., Minneapolis, Minnesota; (800) 735-7323; www.freespiritpublishing.com; all rights reserved.

None of the third parties mentioned within any of this text (with the exception of Free Spirit Publishing, which gave permission to quote one of its works) endorse any part of this book.

(Believe me, they're probably avoiding it like the plague.)

Please Note:

No promises on anything are made within these pages, and I am in no way even remotely liable for anything even remotely related to this book. I cannot be held responsible for any of this. Should you turn the page and get a paper-cut or something, it's so not my fault.

By reading any of this material, you unconditionally agree that you won't be offended by any of it. In fact, even if you think about something while reading it that offends you in any conceivable manner, I'm still not responsible. Yeah, that's right, I just placed a liability on your thoughts. What are you going to do about it? Nothing, because I can't be held accountable.

Don't even put up the pretense of considering suing me. I don't have any money, and I don't hold any responsibility for any of this. Hey, it might just be a coincidence that my name is on the front cover—did you ever think of that? Why don't you try to sue somebody else? The paper of this book was probably made in Thailand; why don't you try to sue them?

Speaking of which, I hold no responsibility for foreign politics of any kind. If I somehow piss off a Communist country, well, that's your fault for being Communist. Where were you when they were handing out democracies? Why don't you go back to feudalism? That's a fun one. And by the way, I've got hidden bunkers that go from here to Atlantis, so it's not like you can find me anyway. Complain to some governmental authority of yours in charge of foreign relations, not to me.

It is also important to mention that I claim every single friggin' right to this book; it's my thoughts, my information, my observations, and my insane ravings. It's mine; I own it. Don't even consider an attempt to think about copying any of the ideas held within. That's right, now I've placed a liability on a precognition of the future. What are you going to do about it? Too late, I already know, and the answer is absolutely nothing. You may spread these ideas to others on my behalf and encourage them to buy a copy of the book, but that's about it. Copyright 2005—intellectual property, biznitch. Legal lawsuits will fly at you faster than a speeding bullet, faster than IRS officers during tax season, faster than Customs at a Palestinian carrying a fake passport at an international airport during Ramadan. How can I claim ownership rights without claiming liability for offenses? That's for the Montana militia to decide.

Thank you for your cooperation.

Table of CONTENTS

Introduction...xv

CHAPTER ONE
Hello, Mr. Morning 1
The Weather, and Why I Don't Like It 4
The Journey of a Thousand Miles Begins (with One Lame
Bus Ride)...6
High School Society Is an Inevitable Torture..........................9
Goths, Freshmen, and Ourselves: We Hate Them All.........11

CHAPTER TWO
Dysfunction Junction, What's Your Function?.....................17
There Once Was a Girl from Naugatuck 19
Weird Word List 20

CHAPTER THREE
Smells Like Homeroom Spirit...23
Amnesty International Has Lost Its Mind 25
Fated to Unplanned Transmutation 28
Miscellaneous Philosophy—Part 1: The Art of Random
Thought 30

CHAPTER FOUR
Biology Class: My Old Arch-Nemesis 33
If You're Going to Pay Attention, You Might as Well Take
Down the Notes 35
What My Handwriting, Leonardo da Vinci, and Jimmy
Carter Have in Common 37
The Metric System: My Other Old Arch-Nemesis...............40
Miscellaneous Philosophy—Part 2: Life's Great Lessons.....43

CHAPTER FIVE
The D-Wing Pilgrimage 45
Classroom from Hell...Literally..47

History Is That Wonderful Thing That Constantly
Reminds Us That We Messed Up 48
World History Was Insane (and So Was the Teacher).........51
All Work and No Learning Makes a History Class..............55
Miscellaneous Philosophy—Part 3: Surplus Time
Hazards 64

CHAPTER SIX
Heigh-Ho, Heigh-Ho, It's Off to Personal Health and
Fitness We Go!...65
Prison Ball...67
All Is Not So Quiet on the Western Front 70
Pillow-Polo: Welcome to the Sanctum of Abaddon.............75
Fight or Flight? Animal Instincts Take Center Stage 76
Incredi-Ball 83
The G.A. Gig 85
The Pleasantly Enjoyable Experience....................................88
Miscellaneous Philosophy—Part 4: You Can Tell That
It Was Written on a Friday 89

CHAPTER SEVEN
Romeo, oh Romeo...Where the Hell Are You?......................96
CAPT (Crappy Ass Preparation Test) Practice 103
CAPTain! We're Breaking Up!...105
Other English Beguilement..109
Miscellaneous Philosophy—Part 5: Televised Wasteland..123

CHAPTER EIGHT
Lunch 125
The Real Guidance Department..128
Moments of Introspection...132
Ye Olde Track 'n' Field...134
An Event Un-Foulds 138
How to Deal with Spare Time..141
Miscellaneous Philosophy—Part 6: I'm Not Required
to Care 147

CHAPTER NINE
Holy Sh*t...I Just Realized How Much I Hate Math..........149

Algebra, Latin, and Incest: Three Things That You'll
  Never Need to Succeed in Life 152
Miscellaneous Philosophy — Part 7: Yes, You Can Quote
  Me on That 161

CHAPTER TEN
¡Hola! ¿Como estás? (Hi! How are you?) 163
¡Yo no estoy de acuerdo! (I disagree!) 169
Miscellaneous Philosophy — Part 8: Too Many Opinions
  for My Own Good 173

THE AFTER CHAPTER
The Bus Ride Home 177
And Now, a Little Something about Anna (Because
  I'm Sure She's Anticipating This) 180
THE Theorem 183
Sixteen Years in the Life 184

ABOUT THE AUTHOR 191

Introduction

"Life's funny like that." Who the hell said that one? The line-of-thought of the statement often disagrees with its context. "A heavily intoxicated man fell face-first into a puddle in Arizona and drowned. Life's funny like that." There's not supposed to be anything funny about death, and—as far as I know—there's not supposed to be anything funny about Arizona. I never thought life was funny like that. You see the bad, the darkness, the depression, the sadness, the pain, the hate, the anger, the forsaken, and the hurtful become the everyday, and you think, "How could any of this be funny?" But then you start to realize what you hadn't before.

"We'll look back on this and laugh," is another one. I don't think any sane person goes to a funeral and says, "Just look on the bright side: Uncle Joe might be dead, but we'll probably look back on all this and laugh." No, you probably won't. No one ever looked back on Watergate and laughed (and those who did laugh did so only out of amusement from the nickname "Tricky Dick"). How could the most terrible of the worst be laughed at, at a different point in time? But then you start to realize what you hadn't before.

LOL—"laugh out loud," for those of you who, like me, never fell into the gaping jaws of online instant messaging communication. I always thought it was kind of weird how we usually associate this phrase with others' suffering. "So then i asked what does he think about u? And he was like, 'I hate that bitch soooo much! LOL!" What the hell's wrong with you? That's hardly something to laugh about, especially out loud. But then you start to realize what you hadn't before.

You start to realize what you've been missing all along—that it was funny because it happened to someone else; it was funny because you lived through it. A thousand different things happen on an average day, and only a few of them can even be considered humorous. So why not laugh while you still have breath to laugh? Don't just laugh at what's funny; laugh at what's ironic. Laugh at the sorrow. Laugh at horror. Laugh at the randomness. Laugh at it all. Laugh out loud. Laugh at death. Die laughing. Maybe everyone else will laugh at your funeral.

One day, I woke up to see that things weren't changing for the better any faster than the polar ice caps were melting. (Kiss my ass, environmentalists.) So I started to laugh. I laughed at how things couldn't possibly get any worse, and then they did. I made jokes and cracked a smile now and then. I made and poked fun, just for the hell of it.

That's what this is all about. I want you to laugh at as many aspects of life as possible. Because laughter makes you think. And thinking makes you laugh. And I want you to think about laughing and laugh about thinking. That's the way things should be. Because I want you to laugh out loud, and I want you to think back to reading this and laugh. Because that's the way it goes— and life's funny like that.

Chapter One

Hello, Mr. Morning

Remember, today is the tomorrow you worried about yesterday.
—Dale Carnegie

How do you start your morning? I start mine in grueling agony, which I think is good to a certain extent. Morning-people scare me. Man was not designed to wake up at dawn, and I don't care what any doctor tells you. "Early to bed and early to rise makes a man healthy, wealthy, and wise"? Well, I've got news for you, Franklin: "Late to bed and late to rise makes a man lazy, crazy, and despised." Wait…that didn't come out right. Wasn't Franklin the one who got shot? I sleep through my American history classes. Or at least, that's what people tell me I slept through. It could have been science class, for all I know. Or a Spanish class. Biology terms are like a foreign language anyway.

I don't know what it is, but there's something about adolescence that just kills me. I get up at five-of-seven—which is probably the latest that the lot of us get up, going by the national average—and sleep through many an afternoon. I can't help feeling a little bit depressed. That youthful energy that gave me the strength to do whatever I wanted, whenever I wanted, has been lost. And to wake up on a weekday morning, at a time that most theologians would deem sacrilegious, and to stop and think for a moment that today I'm going to see people I hate, learn things that I don't want to know, and hear things about people that I never wanted to hear in the first place—then have to do it all over again, day after day, for weeks to come—it's just cruel and unusual. Which also makes it unconstitutional.

1

You see those kinds of people all the time. They're aimlessly wandering the halls, eyes glazed over, listlessly walking from class to class. What time did you get to sleep last night? "Ten." What time did you wake up? "Six." Then they usually push out a small laugh, knowing full well that it doesn't make any sense. I try to look surprised at the unexplainable fatigue, but I'm not. Somewhere I'm thinking that I feel the same way. "In the cockles of my heart," as Denis Leary would say. Then again, there are some that can survive on three hours of sleep every night. Not coincidentally, these are the same people who redefine the meaning of the word "burnout."

When I finally get around to rolling out of bed, I can't help but feel like my life force has been drained. After five years of waking up at this hour, my body still hasn't adjusted to the daily pattern. Some kids make it a point to get up at five in the morning, and then proceed to do some really crazy stuff—like watch the morning news. "The weather report says it's supposed to be cloudy and overcast." Why would you care? You're going to be peregrinating the sheltered halls of an education facility for the next seven hours. Besides, if you sleep a little while longer and then wake up, you won't even need to watch the television to know what the weather for today is going to be. You'll be able to walk outside and pretty much figure it out, connect the dots.

I can never seem to remember what time I fell asleep the night before. Everyone knows what time they go to bed; that's the designated bedtime—that's easy. But the subsequent point at which one falls asleep could be hours after that. Especially someone like me, who has developed some kind of strange insomnia in the last few years. I vaguely remember seeing the clock lighting up the number 1. Maybe it was 1:11 in the morning. Ah crap, I've only had five-and-a-half hours of sleep? I need at least…something more than that.

On most days I wouldn't have a chance in hell of waking up without my alarm clock. I have one of those old-school Nickelodeon alarm clocks that might have been cool when I was eight (or thereabouts). You can set it to the sound you want it to make when it goes off, ranging from military bugles to cuckoo clocks. That doesn't matter to me, though, because what's important to me is the voice that announces that the alarm clock is about to go off. Right before it sounds, a male voice shrouded in static counts down, "Three...two...one..." I always turn it off after I hear that.

But I will not get out of bed until I hear that voice. Sometimes I will, for some reason unbeknownst to me, wake up a few minutes before the alarm goes off. I'll look at the clock to see that the time is 6:53. But I won't get up. I will not and cannot get up to start my day until I hear that voice. In my bewildered and bedraggled state, sometime halfway through my sophomore year, I became convinced that the voice was none other than the voice of Buddha. That's right, it was Buddha himself who was calling me to rise each morning and seek enlightenment. You better watch yourself, or you might wind up with one of these Buddhist alarm clocks someday. The thing makes me paranoid, because Jesus isn't likely to be too happy when he finds out that I've been cheating on him by using another deity to motivate myself.

After that creepy debacle, I pull myself together. I prepare myself in short order for another day at Terryville High School. I say that with a bit of humor, because there's nothing that can really prepare you for Terryville High School, or most high schools, from what I can gather. Nothing except experience.

I quickly slurp a smoothie. I hate smoothies, and to this day my mouth twitches from the very thought of them. Why do I drink them if I detest them so much? Because they're the best thirty-second breakfast possible. Breakfast is, after all, the most important meal of the day. Still, there's nothing that makes them go down any easier. On really bad weeks, when the yogurt has been substituted with cottage cheese, and peaches have been added into the mix (the worst possible combination on the planet), I'll fantasize about eating Lucky Charms over summer vacation. Ooh yeah...hearts, stars, and horseshoes, clovers and blue moons; pots of gold and rainbows, and me red balloons. Summer vacation is so magically delicious when you spend it with Irish stereotypes.

The Weather, and Why I Don't Like It

*There is science, logic, reason; there is thought verified by expe-
rience. And then there is California.*
                                                    —Edward Abbey

Go outside to wait for the frickin' school bus (and that may
very well be the only time that I will use the word "frickin'" for
the duration of the book); during the winter you get to see the sun
rise, but with the insane cold and the sunlight void, it gets old
after a month or so. That may be one of the great disadvantages
of living in New England, never mind Connecticut. The weather
is, simply put, not fun. The winters are terrible, just terrible. You
can get temperatures that reach into the minus-fifteen area, without the windchill. Which is stupid, as the temperature *with* the
windchill is the only temperature that matters. It's the only one
that matters because that's how cold it *feels*. The human body cannot pick anything beyond what we feel. It's kind of like room temperature—it doesn't matter what the temperature of the room is,
it's always room temperature. And believe me, I've gotten into a
lot of arguments with science teachers over that.

Then, there are the summers. In places like—oh, I don't
know—the Arctic, they (the Eskimos and the research scientists)
don't get blasted with a grueling hot summer. However, in New
England, the temperature can get over a hundred in the summer
as well. Dry heat? No, my friend, that's a hundred canolies with
ninety-something percent humidity. "It's freezing in the winter
and broiling in the summer; why would anyone want to live
there?" you ask. Good question. A question that I get to contem-
plate daily, considering that my parents once lived in California—
the good part of California.

The weather is not even remotely predictable, either. It does-
n't follow any kind of pattern. You'll run into a situation where
you get a long, hard (snickers all around), cold, relentless winter
up until February. Then March comes around, and for the entire
first week of March, the temperature is above sixty. That's right,
sixty. Hell, for three days it hit seventy. For a moment, you start
to think, "Hey! Looks like that damn groundhog was wrong!"

Then a month later, in April, you get one of the worst snowstorms ever, and the entire state is shut down for two days.

DAMN YOU PUNXATAUNY PHIL!

DAMN YOU TO HHHEEEEELLLLLLL!!!

The curse of the fur strikes again. As the old saying goes, if you don't like the weather in New England, wait a minute. That's how you can spot the tourists. They're the ones standing outside with stopwatches.

The weather, along with high taxes and a complete lack of culture, is on a mounting list of reasons why Terryville is just not the place to be. If I may stretch that a little bit further, I would also say that Connecticut isn't the place to be. I once read a section of a textbook that proudly declared that Hartford is the insurance capital of the world. And I just thought, y'know, maybe we should just keep that our little secret. No matter—as soon as you move here, you figure it out by all the courtesy calls. I hear that we once had the stock exchange in Hartford. I guess *they* figured that the stock exchange was just too cool for the capital of Connecticut, so *they* moved it to the capital of a cooler state. I'll bet it was the same day that they opened Studio 54. But I can't say that for sure.

Do you know who *they* are? *They* are the system. That's right—the system. An interwoven bureaucracy that controls the lives of all who enter their tangled web of bureaucratic interwoveness. We used to call it "the Man" during the seventies, but I decided that it was about time that the faceless enemy of our nightmares be christened with something that reflects the modern age. *They* would never see that coming. But then again, of course *they* would. After all, *they* ARE the system. The system is everywhere...*Neo, I want to tell you about the system ...*

The Journey of a Thousand Miles Begins
(with One Lame Bus Ride)

Life is just one damned thing after another.
—*Elbert Hubbard*

Slowly but surely (emphasis on the former), the bus lumbers around the corner of my street. By this time I've known that it was coming for a good two minutes. Diesel engines make a distinct sound, like a paper shredder going through a meat grinder. Most of them do. I have to say "most" because I was on one once that was more like a weed-whacker with issues. I hated that damn yellow beast. Who decided to make the school buses yellow, anyway? Weren't the submarines supposed to be yellow? Don't even get me started on the minibuses—the proverbial "tart carts," as it were.

Once I get on the bus, I head straight for the back in order to avoid as many people as possible. It's not that I'm anthropophobic, it's just...oh wait, yes it is. Way in the back is Tom. He's always there. Always. I don't say "hi" and I don't say "good morning." I don't say anything, and even if I did Tom wouldn't respond. Tom is too busy doing homework, or perhaps he may be too busy sleeping. That's just how Tom works. For you see, ladies and gentlemen, Tom acts like a jackass in the morning. Tom acts like a jackass in the afternoon, too. I have no idea how Tom acts in the evening, but I could probably make an educated guess. The first thing you'll notice about Tom is that he's wearing a pair of jeans and a T-shirt. The temperature is way, way below freezing, and he's sitting there with a T-shirt and that stupid, inane look that's completely devoid of expression. If you stare at him long enough, he'll look up at you and very nonchalantly state, "It's chilly this morning."

I'm no meteorologist, but to me the word "chilly" implies something along the lines of fifty degrees with a brisk breeze. For winters in Connecticut, I use the phrase, "Holy shit, it's *fuckin' cold*!" But you've got to resist that urge to argue with Tom. Bickering with Tom is like trying to hassle a brick wall—after a while, you start to feel really stupid while the wall just stares blankly back at you. So I'll sit down, take several deep breaths, and avoid eye contact. "You're not cold, are you?" Shuddup Tom! Just shut up!

In a few minutes, Mike will get on the bus. His first name is Mike and I usually call him Mike, but there are just too many Mikes in my school. Mike is the closest you can get to acting like you're tripping on ecstasy *without* actually tripping on ecstasy. He's usually quiet in the mornings, for some reason. Sometimes he does homework, just like Tom. Sometimes he sleeps, just like Tom. In fact, he sits right in front of Tom. I don't sit anywhere near the freak or the jackass. I sit on the other side of the bus, where it's safe.

The bus stops at a four-way intersection to pick up twenty-something kids. (That's quantity, not age.) Kevin will sit a little ways off, possibly out of fear. Anna will sit with Mike and bother us about whatever. "Isn't it a beautiful day, everyone? It's such a beautiful day!" For some reason, she always seems astounded that we're not very talkative at this hour. Seems unmistakable to us, cabalistic to her. You see, ladies and gentlemen, Anna *is* a morning person, and that *does* scare me.

During our freshman year, that's how the seating arrangement went; every day, no matter what. Once we hit our sophomore year (in a "hit-the-ground-running" fashion), some things changed. Kevin stopped being a regular. Anna—now well accompanied by a vast quantity of upperclassman gentlemen who suited her fancy (her "hot hunnies," as Mike dubbed them)—became more of an afternoon person. But Tom and I can deal with that. Or Tom can. Nothing affects Tom. It irked me in an odd kind of way. I'm still not sure as to why.


```
???????     |    KEVIN
_ _ _ _ _ _ _ _ _ _ _ _ _ _ _ _ -
MIKE & ANNA  |some kid
_ _ _ _ _ _ _ _ _ _ _ _ _ _ _ _ -
TOM         |    STEFAN (the author, stupid)
```

It's mostly quiet in the mornings, and any conversations to be had are stupid ones. Dumb things come up, like Mike discussing some disgustingly nasty girl, asking us if any of us would kiss her for fifty dollars. "I would," he admits.

Time for a quick rebuttal: "Mike, fifty dollars wouldn't even begin to cover the medical expenses that you would incur from the numerous diseases and infections that you would get from making that kind of contact with her. Come to think of it, fifty dollars would be just enough to cover the cost of the WD40 needed to lubricate the wheels on your hospital stretcher as you go rolling by on your way to the emergency room." A decent amount of laughter arises from the back-of-bus crew. Decent for a morning session, at any rate.

The bus pulls up to the high school at around 7:30 a.m. It's a big, cardboard box of a building that's long since been too small and too underfunded to do much of anything. But that's the mentality of the place—not enough for too little. Most schools have three or four floors. Ours has two. I think it was built in 1968, when the town population was around five thousand. Back then, it probably seemed rather spacious. Now it's more like a prison. Perhaps even worse than one—at least there's a large enough cafeteria in the slammer.

We quietly file out in due order. I give a swift punch to Tom's leg to wake him up. He's taken more naps on school buses than Keith Richards has taken drugs. Nah, maybe not. That's a horrible thing to say about Keith Richards. I was going to just leave him there so that he could wake up when the bus arrived at the middle school and realize what a terrible mistake he had made. I was going to. No idea what it was that made me reconsider.

As we walk off the bus, some of the middle school kids (who fill up most of the bus) evade our gaze, while others stare at us uneasily. I don't blame them. I did the same thing when I was at their age. They give you the kind of look you would expect if you were going off to fight a battle that everyone knew you were going to lose. Their eyes are cold, anxious, looking for answers. They watch us tread off the bus and into a building, out of what they know and into the unknown. They watch us depart into a world of the unfathomable, a place they have only heard rumors and stories about. It feels as if they're wondering how we're going to manage this, and how we're going to make it through yet another day of high school life. We put on a straight and serious expression, but deep down we're wondering the same thing. Silence prevails.

High School Society Is an Inevitable Torture

The supreme irony of life is that hardly anyone gets out of it alive.

—*Robert Heinlein*

You walk into the school, and to anyone on the outside it will just look like mass chaos. Words and conversations whiz around in circles and bounce off the walls, like a game of table hockey with a couple of crack addicts. There are kids everywhere—up along the stairway, around the doors, by the office and cafeteria entrances, in front of the girls' locker room at the far end, and everywhere in between.

But it's not chaos. It's all perfectly organized and situated. Everyone has their own specific social group (separated by various sub-factions) and their own specific preferred meeting place. The members of the social group will gather wherever the meeting point is and form a circle (or semicircle, if they happen to be near a wall or other obstruction). The highest-ranked members are part of the inner circle and the lesser members part of the outer. It's an entire social system separate from the rest of the world that has developed on its own over the course of time. I am not one of these "inner" people, as it were. I am what you would call a "filler" person. I stand nearby for the simple purpose of filling any gaps in the circle. Although it may seem menial, it is essential in order to keep the lesser people from reaching the inner people. A thankless job, but someone has to do it. Theoretically.

All of them are moving toward one singular goal: get through the day. Just survive this one day, even if it's only to be able to go home and sleep. It doesn't matter if it's a Monday and they have four more days to go before the weekend, and it doesn't matter if it's only the beginning of the school year and they have many more school days before summer vacation. None of it matters. Because if they can just get through this day, everything is going to be just fine. It's the entire mentality of a generation bound to do four years of academic servitude in the confines of the under-budgeted, brick-and-mortar hellhole that is Terryville High School.

Everyone has a point where they give up. Some of us build up our grade until halfway through the school year, and then coast for the rest. Others try for the first two weeks before they admit defeat. Some are still putting forth their best effort; some haven't tried since eighth grade. That really was the last time that we had everything going for us—the closest we've come to reaching the fabled "glory days" of youth. High school has a lot of perks, but it has a lot of pitfalls, too. The rigid social circles, the uneven peer pressures, and drama in every demonic form you can imagine.

With our graduation from Harry S. Fisher (then immaturely dubbed Harry "Ass" Fisher) Middle School, our once pleasant way of life all at once vanished. Things, in every meaning of the phrase, went to pieces. The social structure shifted and imploded on itself. And so, our conversations were filled with the retelling of stories of what we had done and what we had accomplished during that momentous year. "Do you remember when …?" was something that we all said and reminisced about. During a lull in conversation, someone would bring up this thing or that thing, reaching back to a bygone era. It feels like it all happened so long ago.

I think this may have been the reason why there was such a dramatic change in our attitude and work ethic during our early high school years. The sense of how great things used to be was replaced by a widespread mood of doom and gloom. The ever-constant thought of "Why bother?" plagued us daily, and we slowly gave up on the seemingly endless struggle to do better and achieve what we were convinced was out of our reach. We started to lose control.

All of this leads to an overwhelming mutual sense of apathy, lethargy, and indifference to everything. I suppose you could call it premature senioritis—a disease for which there is no known cure. And so, the downward spiral of rampant cheating; ever-lessening concern about our academic careers; and a newfound, deep-seated mistrust of the system began. Judging by what I know from talking with people from other classes, we aren't the first ones to be experiencing this, either.

I think most of us have gotten over the old memories by now. I believe that we've finally received the "closure" that we need. We've accepted our destiny, and are determined to make do with these new circumstances. Still, sometimes you can't help but think back...thinking about when things were better. Behind all of it is some kind of desire, I'm sure of it. Some kind of weird social pressure to reach a level of status that we will never be able to attain. That's what it always felt like to me. No matter what you do, you'll always be a step lower than what you wanted. Sad but true. No punchline involved.

Goths, Freshmen, and Ourselves: We Hate Them All

Love your enemies just in case your friends turn out to be a bunch of bastards.
　　　　　　　　　　　　　　　　　—*R. A. Dickson*

The first bell rings at 7:40 a.m., and slowly the entire school populace of five hundred or so starts to mass migrate toward their lockers. One of the unfortunate facts of life that will quickly become painfully evident is the utter hallway infestation of freshmen and Goths. These people are everywhere in ever-growing numbers.

The freshmen have long since been considered unavoidable as far as societal entities go. Everyone hated my class (class of 2006) when we were freshmen. The reasons for newbie animosity are the same as they've always been: We crowd the corridors; we fill up all the good electives (e.g. Foods); we can't make the transition into older, more mature subjects of both discussion and involvement. One of the most well-documented phenomenons is that of incoming girls being overwhelmed by upperclassmen guys. Their eagerness to charge this new dating scene and participate in previously objectionable (and unmentionable) activities leads to what we like to denominate as the "freshman whore." My class was no exception. We broke all the freshman whore records ever made. Much to our dismay, the following freshman class proceeded to break most of those records. The future seems forlorn and saturnine when you think about what next year's class is going to be like.

Admittedly, even I hated my freshman class during my freshman year. However, during our time as sophomores it became rather noticeable that the situation was fast getting out of control. The graduating class of 2003 had about 108 students, give or take a few. When class of 2007 came in the following year, that number had jumped to 167. And this was not exactly what you would call 167 of the best and brightest. By the end of the first term, eighty-three of them, roughly 50 percent, were failing one or more classes. None of them seemed to care. I should also mention that if you fail so much as one class during your freshman year, you don't go on to become a sophomore. If that doesn't scream "hopeless," I don't know what does. In the words of one of our guidance counselors, "Our freshman class has issues."

That's another thing about freshman classes. Just when you think that they couldn't possibly get any worse, you see the next freshman class, and quietly concede to yourself, "I stand corrected." That's the natural progression of things—the Theory of Evolution in reverse. The more and more I familiarize myself with today's teenage culture and read about oral sex hookups, friends with benefits, and thirteen being the new eighteen, the more I think that all future generations (meaning, all those born after 1988) are doomed (or fucked, depending on how you read it). The lot of us in our class believe that we have reached the floor as far as the theory goes. We have collectively decided amongst ourselves that we are the world's last hope—after us, there's nothing left. One day, while speaking to Tom, I mentioned that, "Y'know, Tom, once the last of our generation dies, the world is going to end."

He looked at me, smiled, and simply said, "Yeah, I know."

Then there is the other rapidly growing-at-the-rate-which-rodents-breed band of individuals who we commonly refer to as the Goths. The old interpretation of a Gothic person was that of someone who had a deep punk rock influence, an extensive wardrobe of black clothing, and who didn't conform to the standard way of society. These were the people who never participated in anything whatsoever. To some extent, this definition still holds true. However, it used to be that Gothic people, because of their perceptible dark influence and refusal to conform, were at one point something that was desirable, from what I can gather from old archives. Nowadays you can even find porn sites that feature "Goth girls" showing off their badass attitude (along with several other things).

At Terryville, though, the term Goth was used to shun these select groups of people whenever possible. I suppose, in a way, they were Gothist extremists. In addition to not conforming to the traditional aspects of society, such as sports, a good deal of them decided to not abide by the idea of bathing regularly. The choices of clothing varied from striped stockings, to fishnet, to stuff straight out of the Trenchcoat Mafia's spring catalog. I recall one particular Goth coming to school in a chicken suit. The color of their hair changed almost weekly, and a good lot of them were rumored to embrace Satan. Although no actual statistics have ever been kept about the Goths' numbers, it has been estimated that the number of Goths in Terryville High School from 2002 to 2004 has, at the very least, doubled.

The whole societal evolution of Gothism is what freaks me out. Back in the day, the entire social order was primarily made up of cliques. They were the building blocks of the societal pyramid, if you will. The Goths used to be the rebels, the ones who refused to be conformists of the clique tradition. It isn't like that anymore. The number of Goths has increased to such a degree that they are now a clique in their own right. The once-outcasts of society are now a completely separate society. Who is left to fight the establishment if even its once most-ardent fighters have given in to demands? What hope is there for the rest of us, who are now left to continue the struggle by ourselves? Alone?

But do you know what I really want to know? Whether or not Gothism is a disease or an error in the genetic makeup. If it's a disease, perhaps there might be a way to be vaccinated for it. We can find a cure, or at least keep it from spreading. However, if it's a genetic problem, we'll need concentration camps of some sort. Either that or a new law that allows us to deport them to the north. Let the Canadians deal with the ravages of Gothism, I say. It's all outlined in my modest proposal.

There is always the temptation to rule out the entire sequence as something that is undesirable. As if this is something that we could all agree to hate. But the irony of the loathing of groups such as the Goths and the freshmen is that our revulsion of them, in and of itself, is not what made them unique. If you were to wipe away all the smiling faces, common lies, and farewell funny jokes, you'd discover that no one really liked anybody. You could start talking shit about someone else while in the conversational circle, but as soon as you left, people would start talking shit about *you*. We were all guilty of it. In our own way, we all trusted the wrong people. We trusted the people who listened to our ranting and complaining. And the reason they listened was because they were waiting for us to leave before they started talking. The superciliousness of the upper crust of the populace leads to a very interesting paradigm: All the kids who were presumably beneath the rest were really the ones who were worth knowing, and the jackanapes who everyone professed to want to be a part of were the ones who should have been ostracized. But most of you who are going through public high school probably already know this.

I was rarely one of these people. After entering high school, I quickly developed this innate ability to put on a somewhat happy face, force a smile, and coerce small talk without anyone else figuring out that deep down, I was secretly damning the lot of them to Hell. You have to do that, or else you'll be surrounded daily by people asking you, "What's wrong?" Yeah, as if they could help. My instincts were what allowed me to quickly develop an inherent mistrust of everyone. That was really the whole story of what we did. Like little kids, we played make-believe to fool ourselves into thinking that everything was okay, and that everything was going to be just fine. We sunk ourselves as deep as we could into drugs, sex, and lies, and then surrounded ourselves with people who we called friends in order to make it appear that everything was going great in every way possible. I once heard someone in the halls say, "We're juniors in high school! *Sex* is going to happen!" People really need to learn how to use their indoor voices to better effect.

Into this ocean of deceit we descended, never thinking that anything could possibly go wrong. Never thinking that, at some point, we would have to come up for air. Kids these days ...

Chapter Two

Dysfunction Junction, What's Your Function?

I hate to advocate drugs, alcohol, violence, or insanity to anyone, but they've always worked for me.
—Hunter S. Thompson

I'll make my way upstairs to my locker. There are two different kinds of lockers—the big ones and the small ones. The small ones are kind of like your kindergarten cubby, stretched lengthways. You'll be lucky if you can put a jacket into them, let alone a backpack (or knapsack, or messenger bag, or carry-on luggage, or book bag, or packback, or dufflebag, or sackknap, or whatever the hell it is you call it). Then there are the big ones, which are strikingly similar to a walk-in humidor without the "humidor" part. You can fit your back dealie, several jackets, lunches, ten to twenty books, and a week's-worth of laundry. I have one of the big ones. People tell me that I suck ass.

I hate to put people down and lower their self-esteem, but...actually, that's a lie. I couldn't care less about you people. Screw you and your low self-esteem. I'm keeping the school counselors employed. Anyway, some of these people have a habit of doing stuff to be cool. And those who say they're not just doing it to be cool, those are the ones who are *really* doing it just to be cool. Then again, I'm not sure what it is to be cool. I, myself, am starting to hate us no-good teenagers. This aside, nobody before 1996 had a dysfunctional family. I mean, real people who had real dysfunctional families had dysfunctional families, but not the rest of us.

But as soon as that word entered our vocabulary, all of a sudden everyone has a dysfunctional family. There isn't a normal person left on earth who doesn't have a dysfunctional family. Do you know why? Because "dysfunctional" is a big word. Wow, four syllables. Not only is it big, which makes us sound smart, but we kinda know what it means, too. Now, not only do you sound smart, but you *feel* smart. Well, to other retarded people like you, you sound smart. To smart people like me, you just sound retarded. The only dysfunctional part of my family was me. In the meantime, my parents (and I'm sure that there are others out there like them) decided that the best thing for me was to keep me away from every evil factor of life that was trying to creep in.

The biggest argument that I can make against parents trying to overprotect their children is public schools. As far as I'm concerned, overprotecting your kid is like trying to kill them from the inside out. It's also a waste of time. You could spend years and years shielding your offspring from every harsh reality that exists and then some. You may have never cursed in front of them, never let them watch the six o'clock news, and given them the most innocent upbringing possible. But as soon as they enter a public high school, your pious hopes will be taken by the throat, choked to death, chopped into little pieces, and packaged into the next batch of Won Ton soup. Because as soon as they enter a public high school, the clock starts counting down until the time that they meet that one person who didn't have that perfectly normal childhood. Those select few who had to suffer through some of the worst that the world has to offer at an exceptionally young age are going to be the ones who will completely change your child's way of thinking.

There Once Was a Girl from Naugatuck

You know your children are growing up when they stop asking you where they came from and refuse to tell you where they're going.

—*P. J. O'Rourke*

I met the person who would be destined to change my way of thinking in seventh grade, so I got a full year-and-a-half jump on the sadistic average. Her name was Kate, and she would tell me one of the most fascinating stories that I've ever heard: the story of her life.

I hadn't the slightest clue of what she had been through when I first met her in my computer class, way back when. She looked just like any other girl you might meet. Blonde hair, blue eyes, good sense of humor, athletic...ravishing. Maybe even a little sexy. Maybe even a lot. It would be much later, though—once we started high school—when I really started to get to know her. As it turned out, she was not like just any other girl you might meet. She was different in many ways. First, she was frequently beset by medical problems, the most prominent of which was hypoglycemia, a condition that results in an abnormally low blood-sugar level. When it becomes too low, the consequence is light-headedness and fainting. A nuisance, you might imagine, especially when fainting while going up or down stairs.

She once told me that she was always nervous about making first impressions because there were so many facets to her personality. After spending four years getting to know her, I don't doubt that one bit. It's most likely the aftermath of spending a life-long effort to get through life. Her mother had her when she was just nineteen. Her father, then a heavy drug addict, divorced her mother three years later. Kate was further jolted by a series of abrupt moves: first from Naugatuck to Waterbury, then to Terryville. She spent the fourth grade in Florida, but only the fourth grade. In the midst of all this, her mother got remarried and had two more kids.

This influx of mixed feelings is undoubtedly what caused her intense mood swings, mainly shifting between hotheaded, bloody-minded anger to deep-seated, black dog depression. She didn't adapt to those emotional reroutes too well, either, as evidenced by her four suicide attempts, made between ages of ten and thirteen. Each time it was something different. First by ingesting chemicals, followed by an attempted drowning, then by cutting herself, and then by overdosing on pills. Each time she brought herself a little bit closer to the ultimate goal of escaping the Hell that seemed to encompass her life, and each time she was saved at the last moment from the icy grasp of Death.

By the time I had met her, she had worked through all of it. I can't imagine what it would have been like if I had met her sooner.

Today, Kate is alright. The rage, despondency, and thoughts of death have long since passed her. To me, she is an inspiration to keep going in the face of all odds, because no matter how bad you think it is now, it can always get so much worse. She's living proof that life can be far from normal and average. And no amount of protection can keep you from knowing the truth about how cruel life can be. By now I suppose I'm a little jaded, because I've heard all the horror stories. There are no innocent people left. Stories of divorces, beatings, attempted suicides, prison, drugs, pregnancy—all of them before the age of fifteen. And every single person who has told me their story, they all had one thing in common. They all said, "There's no need to feel sorry for me."

"Why wouldn't we feel sorry for them?" They told us not to. "Why would they tell us that?" Why are you trying to communicate to someone through a book? Perhaps you should see a doctor about that. And if the words start going weird on you, you're probably tripping on ACID and should lie DoWn first until that lizArd turns bAck into a lampshAde.

Weird Word List

This is the official Miscellaneous Philosophy Weird Word List, compiled over many minutes by the creative genius of Mike and Stefan. Whenever you're feeling down, or depressed, or want to commit suicide and have a loaded gun pointed at your head, just read off each of the following words aloud to yourself, and you're guaranteed to feel better immediately. If you don't, then go ahead and pull the trigger because you're not human anyway:

Denominator
Hippopotamus
Biblical
Falafel (pronounced like "waffle" with a flare to it)
Booklet
Syphilis
Flabbergasted
Coccyx
Biblical Booklet
Paradigm (pretend that the "g" isn't silent)
Euphemism
Expectorate
Rectum
Sphinx
Esophagus
Pistachio
Ethiopian
Caboose
Ambiguous
Ostrich
Kazakhstan
Kibbutz
Saskatchewan
Emu
Moustache
Squelch
Meniscus
Kaput
Thwack

See? Now don't you feel better already? (BAM!)

Chapter Three

Smells Like Homeroom Spirit

While there's life, there's hope.

—Cicero

As the various groups congregate and prepare for a new day of half-assing, there comes a point when each member must bid farewell, and journey to their homeroom. In order to make this parting more sweet and less sorrowful, every constituent will leave simultaneously. There is no discussion about this, nor is there any set time. Everyone in the group knows when the moment has come, and each person departs at once. I, too, take my leave at this point and walk a relatively short distance to my own colloquium for attendance purposes.

My sophomore homeroom is also a math room. Each time I stroll in my body reminds me that it's a math room by sending a sharp chill down the length of my spine and by giving orders for my neurological system to go into panic mode. Nothing unusual really, just my body's methodical reaction to math. It used to be worse, but the therapy really helped in limiting the vomiting and the shouting of "The devil is upon us! Run for your lives!" Needless to say, that parochial school experience was exceptionally brief.

Slowly I meander toward my desk and lower myself into the attached chair. While doing so, I put as much effort as possible into not looking at the surface of the desk. Why? Because the countertop of this shoddy piece of furniture, along with all the others in the room, is covered in solutions to logarithms. While the chart is undoubtedly useful to anyone who can interpret the erratic collection of numbers, to anyone else it is just an eyesore. Hundreds and hundreds of figures, ever-so-slightly increasing from one to the next by a hundred-thousandth of a decimal, make for an immensely grueling ordeal for the corneas of any bipedal human. Taken all together, they bear a striking resemblance to the old stock market ticker:

9.00673

9.00675

9.00678

Sell! Sell!

If you ever wanted to know what it's like to take some really bad acid, just stare into the desk cross-eyed for about five minutes. On second thought, don't. No way I'm getting sued for something as stupid as that.

Brianna will walk in right about now. She's one of Terryville High School's star basketball/volleyball/tennis players, and, in spite of her small, four-foot-eleven stature (over a foot below from where I stand), she can easily nail shot after shot from the three point line (as well as set up for a spike and trade volleys). I can't help but admire athletes, probably because I'm such an abysmal failure as one. Bri, being that idyllic amalgamation of half-hysterical idealist and brutally honest pragmatist, always struck me as someone who wasn't afraid to take on the world, but didn't think that the rewards were worthwhile in the long run—which is probably true.

We casually exchange hellos, me with a half-insincere sarcastic quality, and her with a distinct tone that lets me know that she's happy to see me, but vividly states that she's pissed that she has to spend yet another day in school. It's a very enchanting tone, if nothing else. Homework seems to be her biggest distraction, as she's constantly laboring intensely to finish this ditto or that paper before time runs out. I'm usually doing the same thing. Every now and then you'll see her put down her pencil, heave a huge sigh, look up with a broad, beaming smile, and proudly declare, "*Fuck* this *shit*. No way I'm doing this." I love the way she swears—all the emphasis on all the right words. Or, for no plausible reason, she'll come in and start voicing her opinions of people. "People in this school are so *gay*. I hate them so much. I just can't stand them." A girl after my own heart.

Quietly, patiently, I sit passing the few minutes that are left before the last bell rings—the last bell that will formally announce that our daily drudgery has begun. It does. A loud, piercing, high-pitched buzz that reverberates off the walls and minds of all present. Its assuredly guiltless tintinnabulation almost disguises the enslavement that we must now endure. Almost.

The regular tradition of morning announcements (via the local closed-circuit television channel) proceeds posthaste. A number of different messages are delivered on the morning announcements, and if I bothered to listen to them once in awhile, I just might have an idea of what they are. Just maybe.

What always bothers me the most about the morning announcements are the endless number of clubs and school-sponsored organizations promoting themselves on the television in the guise of calling it an announcement. They are no such things. They are shameless self-advertising, taking advantage of the fact that they, in theory, have 100 percent of their target audience—students at Terryville High School. And none of these are worse than Amnesty International.

Amnesty International Has Lost Its Mind

Only two things are infinite: the universe and human stupidity. And I'm not sure about the former.
—Albert Einstein

Amnesty International is one of the worst organizations ever to festoon the face of the planet. Most people usually associate the Nazis with that kind of remark, and I do, too, but I think this one is right up there. Sure, they're not creating world war or executing millions of Jews—they don't believe in execution, and that really wouldn't be their style anyway. But I'm not about to give them an automatic absolution just because they're not the absolute worst that human nature has to offer. That's what we did with Stalin, and we all know how that worked out. (Thank you, George Orwell.)

Their intentions might be good and honorable, but everything else is rotten to the core. This became painfully evident during "Amnesty International Awareness Week." That's right, an entire week during which its members can bitch about whatever they feel like bitching about. One of these little not-so-well-known facts is that there are over 200,000 land mines still active across the world. That's terrible! What should we do about it, Amnesty International? "No idea! We just wanted to make you aware of that! After all, it's Amnesty International *fuckin'* Awareness Week!" You bastards. If you don't have a plan of action, then don't complain. Pure and simple. I don't like land mines either, but since I have no idea how to fix the problem, I'm not going to bring it up. The least you can do is have the common courtesy to follow suit. It's still not as bad as when they put X's on the floor tiles with masking tape, claiming that if you stepped on them, you were stepping on a land mine, and therefore would be killed instantly. As if we give a rat's ass. I died twice in ten seconds flat.

I remember one week, the kids that do the announcements came on, and one of them starting going off on a civil war that was taking place in the Congo. Wonderful! Now what? Well, they want us to sign a petition. A petition? You fuckin' morons! That won't do *anything*! You're dealing with Central African dictators, and if there's one thing that I know about Central African dictators, it's that they don't give a *shit* about what some two-bit group of high school students think about them! In the words of Bri, "These guys are gonna look at this petition thing and think, 'Hey! Now I've got something to wipe my ass with!'" I couldn't have said it better myself.

Just take a moment to consider what you're talking about: the Congo. The Congo is a country that changes its name at least once every three years. First, it was the "Congo." Then, it was "Zaire." Then, it was the "Democratic Republic of the Congo." That alone should tell you something. A civil war in the Congo is not some sort of international crisis—it's just Thursday.

Then there was someone (no names now, no names) who asked me if I had signed the petition. When I told her no, she had the courage (but not the brains) to tell me, "Well, I signed the petition!" Oh, this was just too much. Trying to be as calm as I could, I formulated my reply. "Let me try to explain something to you:

signing the petition to stop the violence in the Congo will *not* stop the violence in the Congo. It *will* waste ink. It *will* waste your time, but it will *not* stop the violence in the Congo." I think I got my point across.

If they were trying to enlist people for a militia to go fight the rebels in the Congo, *then* I would say, "Fine. Christ be with you." But a petition? Have you lost what little sense you have left? If there's one thing I've learned about life, it's that stupidity is evil. And *this* organization, ladies and gentlemen, is, by definition, *evil*.

I thought that after several long, harrowing days, the fiasco with the Congo and our sudden need to save it was over. But I was wrong—it wasn't. Later that week, I strolled into school and found that the main hall had been blockaded with tables, and that the Amnesty International posse, most of whom were Gothist extremists, had infested the area like Trekkies at an annual convention. Most of them were plastering people with stickers with various meaningless slogans and practically forcing people to sign the petition. Most people signed and took the stickers just so that they would be let through. Not me, though. When they came at me with stickers, I told them "No! *Get back...back I say*! Back! You put those stickers on *your* sheet! I am walking away!"

You should have seen some of these stickers: "STOP THE VIOLENCE IN THE CONGO," "SAVE THE CONGO," etcetera, etcetera. I don't get it. Honestly, what were they trying to accomplish? Let's pretend, for a second, that Amnesty International somehow manages to get every student in the school to wear a sticker on their shirt that asks others to stop the violence in the Congo. Now what? Before there was nothing but atrocious violence, and now we've got atrocious violence with *stickers*! The fuck?! And meanwhile, all throughout their entire tirade of lost causes, they're plastering people with stickers, plastering the hallways with flyers—why not save the rainforest, Amnesty International? Don't you care about the rainforest?—they're taking over the intercom system and have complete control of the local television broadcasts, and I'm thinking, "Why isn't someone trying to stop them?! For the love of Buddha, why isn't someone trying to stop them?!" Do you know what I did? I made my own sticker. Do you know what it said?

NUKE THE CONGO!

Damn straight. That made me feel a lot better. One member of the student body, Jen by name (whom I will explain in further detail later), asked me in condescending disdain, "So, do you feel like a jerk wearing that sticker?"

"Not any more than you feel like a whore wearing that skirt," I quietly whispered under my breath. When I went to my history class that day, just about every kid was staring at my chest. It was the closest that I've ever come to feeling like Anna in my life. Ever.

Fated to Unplanned Transmutation

Friendship is born at that moment when one person says to another: 'What! You too? Thought I was the only one.'
— *C. S. Lewis*

But enough about that. The first order of business every morning is to stand and recite the Pledge of Allegiance. While almost everyone will stand (with the exception of Bri), absolutely no one will say the pledge. An eerie silence will befall the room, with the only ones speaking being the kids on television, the homeroom teacher, and occasionally Bri, who will go along with the whole patriotic charade out of mockery more than obligation to anyone, be they country, administration, or otherwise. Once again, King Apathy reigns supreme.

After a brief, fleeting moment of silence, the school populace will seat themselves and either chitchat with everyone else or frantically finish their homework that's due first period. Brianna and I are among the ones making small talk. She chatters mostly of whatever insane English paper has recently been assigned and her plans to put every piece of work off until the last minute. The proper and gentlemanly thing to do would be to reassure her that everything will be fine, that every day gives our lives new opportunities to take advantage of, and that the minor inconveniences of day-to-day life mean little in the grand scheme of things—but I'm not the type of guy who likes to prevaricate about reality. So instead, we'll sit and talk aimlessly, both eagerly awaiting and dreading the last bell at eight o'clock. With its fateful ring, we will depart into the halls, each of us going our own separate ways, and journey to our first class of the day that now stretches ages before us. Quietly we wish, hope, and pray that we will have the energy to make it through. Make it out alive.

The whole homeroom experience is one of those little, insignificant episodes of existence that, in its own method, shapes our own human nature. In so many small ways, it shifts and changes our mode of thinking, to the point that the mind can only imagine what one word, one action, one small trivial thought at one time or another so extensively made us reconsider what the truth really was. Like a car without any side windows, we're charmed and enchanted by what lies on the road ahead without ever thinking to enjoy where we're at that very moment.

Likewise, I sit here thinking about this day in front of me and filled with thoughts about all the days that I've already been through. Every single passing moment races with a thousand recollections, searching feverishly for something, *something* that will give it all meaning, that will allow it all to make sense. What if all this searching and soul-seeking was in vain? What if what I was looking for was right in front of me the entire time? What if happiness was this simple concept that wasn't really so far out of reach as I thought it was? What if I could just find someone…that someone who allows me to see what I've been missing while spending countless days searching? What I've been missing…what I've been missing …

… I never realized how beautiful Brianna is. That curly, light auburn hair, so intricately entwined with blonde highlights. Those deep, blue-green eyes…you could get lost forever in those eyes. A fragrance of fresh flowers encircles her, like an aura of pure felicity. I fidget in my seat, contemplating every possible outcome, every possible causatum, and at the same time weighing all the advantages and disadvantages. Repositioning my pose once, then twice, I try to prepare the words that will make the whole situation run smoothly. The mind bubbles and overflows with the thoughts of possibilities. The muscles twitch with a mixture of excitement and fear. Is it love? Fate? Destiny? Or is this whole dilemma something that was never supposed to happen in the first place? Am I paving the path to my own demise?

Every day you think that you might want to take advantage of the opportunities that are right in front of you. Every day you think that you should look out that side window, be the passenger for once instead of the driver, and see how beautiful the world is. Sometimes I think that I should look at the beautiful world that has been right in front of me for so long. Because there has to be something that gives everything significance. There has to be some sort of *purpose* to all of this. Perhaps I've been closer to that that purpose than I thought I was...Perhaps I should say something to make it all come true ...

"Brianna?"

RIIIIIIIIIIIIINNNNNNNNNNNGGGGGGGGGGGGGGGG!!!

"Yeah?"

"Nothing."

And as she gathers her things to leave, she quietly answers my hardhearted indifference to my own human emotion with, "Have a good day, Stefan."

"You too, Bri...you too."

Well, maybe today's not the day for life-altering decisions (despite Monster.com's insistence that it is).

Miscellaneous Philosophy—Part 1
The Art of Random Thought

For every little subject and opinion of mine that I've managed to cram into this book, there are always a few themes that didn't quite fit in anywhere else. That's why there are a bunch of pages like this one. Perish the thought that you don't get enough of what I think.

We are limited only by our imaginations! ...
and gravity, definitely gravity.

Can you think of all the terms that are used to describe the over-consumption of alcohol? We have oiled, tanked, plowed, befuddled, fuddled, muddled, seeing double, flushed, lush, drunk, totaled, juiced, stewed, polluted, boozed up, buzzed, drunken, jugged, liquored up, on a bun, crocked, sotted, potted, groggy, sloshed, zonked, bombed, bear goggles on, blotto, soaked, hosed, stoned, overcome, comatose, gassed, bashed, trashed, canned, plastered, hammered, tight, high, pie-eyed, flying high, bleary-eyed, merry, jolly, wobbly, tipsy, lit, delirious, in orbit, shit-faced, laced, glazed, wasted, intoxicated, inebriated...the list goes on and on. How do you feel about American society? I, for one, feel pretty good.

Lower Standards = Higher Self-Esteem

When Edmund Hillary was thirty-three years of age, he became the first person to climb to the summit of Mount Everest, the highest point on the planet at twenty-nine thousand, thirty-five feet, seven inches.

They say that once you get into your twenties, your metabolism starts to slow down. Seeing as how I'm currently on a five thousand-calorie diet, this scares me a great deal. One of my greatest fears is that once I'm in my twenties and after a day of my usual food consumption, my metabolism will suddenly and unexpectedly drop, and overnight I'll balloon to three times my normal size, like some kind of fuckin' puffer fish. I'll wake up the next morning, "Oh shit! My metabolism dropped...I'm glad work is downhill. I'll be able to roll there."

Don't worry about Hell. It's a dry heat.

We've all heard of pyromaniacs, but have you ever met klepto-pyromaniacs? People who habitually steal stuff to start fires? Now there's a fun bunch.

Chapter Four

Biology Class: My Old Arch-Nemesis

If you're not confused, you're not paying attention.
— Tom Peters

You can't see it in the halls. You can't smell or taste it. But you can feel it. Oh, how you can feel it. You can feel the dry emotion, cold depression, hot anger, and the hopes, dreams, aspirations, sadness, disappointment, and exhaustion of every student that fills the corridors. It hangs in the air, thicker than the worst of fogs. It hangs in dark patches over every kid's head. Probably the worst part of it is having to walk through it. And of course, you will have to walk through it. All day. For at least six hours.

First on the grueling day ahead of us all is biology. It's not that bad. Which is just as well to say it's not that good, either. Just keep in mind that the entire class is one giant divergence into how the species of every animal on this planet (including those that are extinct) are better than humans. Our biology teacher frequently reminds us that we are destroying the planet and ourselves with our technology, that the human race will be in a large competition with itself for food in several hundred years (though the way he said it you'd think that it would be in several days), that we're not nearly as adaptable as far more superior organisms (such as insects), that we are expeditiously running out of raw materials and fossil fuels, and therefore are going to decline in rapid secession unless some drastic changes are made, preferably within the next five minutes. He somehow linked this to America's foreign policy, every major flaw in our government system, and the downtrodden blue-collar worker. Can you understand why I hate

33

environmentalists? Can you at least understand why I hate biology class?

A student will wind up taking about one-and-a-half pages of
notes per week. Which is something like two-and-three-quarter
gibbets in metric. That is, unless you're like some of these other
people who just photocopy someone else's notes. I'm not saying
that it's a boring class. Well, I am, but it's just that with all the
other things that we have to deal with on a daily basis, it's nice to
be able to space-out for once through something that's largely
irrelevant. Or at least you try to. We have a biology teacher who
is a little out there. Good teacher, mind you. I just think that when
God was handing out brains, our biology teacher got one that had
a little label on it that said, "Do Not Use if Seal is Broken." And it
was. And he did.

It does keep things interesting. Every now and then, you'll be
dozing, trying to find a comfortable position at the impossibly
uncomfortable desks. I had one of these old school desks left over
from the sixties (as evidenced by the substandard workmanship)
in the back of the room. The seat was a bland, yum-yum yellow
shade, and the legs curved down and around the basket. It was
more or less a table mounted on top of a sled. The temptation to
steal it and take it down a frozen, snow-covered hill was enormous. (Unfortunately, someone else stole it before I got the
chance. Possibly one of the janitors.) You're sitting back there,
your eyes barely open, your head pressed against the side bar as
you slouch down as far as possible. You're just at that point that
you might fall asleep, and you hear the teacher say something
like, "People! It's hard to kill a deer with a stick!" Okay, I'll bite—
what is it that you're trying to teach?

You would be amazed as to how easy it is to fall asleep in that
class. At no time was it easier than at the beginning of the year,
when the heat of summer and the wearisome lecture of the day
made for an unmitigated snooze-fest. "Fallasleepa-palooza," if
you will. No matter how hot it was outside, it was forbidden to
open the windows, so as to not let the hot air in. This, in our
instructor's logic, kept the room cooler. How, then, did it become
the most sweltering enclosure in the entire school? I'm not sure if
this guy is familiar with the theory of the greenhouse effect, but I
think someone should enlighten him. The whole thing made

drowsiness unavoidable. I remember sitting there in the back of the room on one such day, during fourth period. We weren't allowed to put our heads down on the desk, so I was doing my best to prop my head to the side on my right arm. In that position, the Sandman was more than happy to come over and slap me silly.

What felt like several hours later, I awoke from an otherworldly getaway. My first speculation was that, judging by what my senses told me, it was sixth period, and that this day was lasting for several eons on end. I then noticed that I was considerably famished, and wondered to myself as to how I could have possibly forgotten to eat lunch during fifth. Then I looked at the clock. "Dammit! We're still here? We've been here *forever!*" Two years of high school was all it took to mess up every aspect of my sleep cycle. At the same time, my dreams started becoming more realistic and reality started becoming more unreal. Yes, I will admit it. Call me crazy, but I'm having more and more difficulty distinguishing the difference between what's reality and what's not. I hope this book is real, because the last time I became rich and famous, I woke up.

If You're Going to Pay Attention, You Might as Well Take Down the Notes

When reviewing your notes before an exam, the most important will be illegible.
— *First Law of Applied Terror*

Taking notes was never big on my list of things that I like to do. Something about taking down information that I never wanted to know in the first place, putting it into such utter shorthand that it becomes completely illegible, writing on some random piece of paper that in the minutes immediately following the end of the class will be lost in the depths of oblivion of my notebook never seemed like a very appealing proposition. Of course, I'll never see it again until the night before that major test so that the odd collection of scribbles and haphazard lines can be analyzed and studied so that mankind (or more specifically, me) will be able to once again uncover their hidden meaning. Kind of like Indiana Jones examining an ancient manuscript that holds the secret to eternal knowledge.

"Let's see here, it appears to be a triangle with turrets, so I'm guessing that that's an 'A' followed by an 'X,' an 'O,' and an 'N,' so that would spell 'axon.' Yes! AXON! These are definitely my notes on the nervous system! Judging by the type of ink used and the layers of dust covering it, I'd say this would date all the way back to early November, but we'll have to use the carbon dating to verify that."

You can always tell which class was boring by all the little drawings that are at the bottom or in the margins of the paper. The more complex the drawing, the more boring the class. The first day of taking notes in the beginning of the year, everything is nice and simple. The important points are bulleted, the diagrams are clear and concise, and there are no drawings to be seen. Then things start getting progressively worse. The writing becomes lopsided and twisted. Which is a bad thing, because now my biology observations are indistinguishable from my Spanish annotations. (Weren't those fun words?) Things begin to forsake the natural order of things as facts begin to fade in and out of reality. The diagrams seem lackadaisical, with arrows swooping in and out to make up for the fact that the terms don't appear anywhere near their corresponding part.

This is immediately obvious when the teacher decides to take a break from teaching (hooray!) in order to check our notebooks (dammit!). Slowly, he meanders down the aisle, like a great Colossus that doth stride the world. "Nice, Matthew. Very good, Mike. Stefan! What the hell happened?!...Either that's a picture of an animal cell or a horrific car accident!"

Then the smart-ass in me speaks up, "The latter, sir." I was perfectly aware that my pitiful excuse for the blueprint of a basic life form walked a thin line between science purposes and Taoism philosophy. And as any astrophysicist can tell you, that is a *very thin line*. Just like the thin line between a porno and a shampoo commercial.

What My Handwriting, Leonardo da Vinci, and Jimmy Carter Have in Common

So about those meaningless drawings and doodles that I spoke of: At first, their presence is minimal. Perhaps an eccentricated star here, an over-glorified asterisk there. Then they start materializing everywhere. Inane little nothings that weave in-between the bindings and lettering. They keep increasing and increasing, until by the time you get to the notes on Anatomy and Physiology, you've got the giant Ying Yang going on with a bunch of other little Chinese do-dads and gonads. I didn't write down the specific date that I took them, but the inscriptions seem to say that I took these particular notes during the Week of the Rat. If you look at it cross-eyed long enough, it almost looks like Jimmy Carter's head. Or perhaps something that Leonardo da Vinci would have sketched while on Prozac. Then again, I'm a sucker for a good Prozac joke.

My handwriting was always something that got to my teachers. Well, to be fair, it only really got to my biology teacher. My freshman physical science teacher had worse handwriting than I did, even though I wrote in cursive and he wrote in print. My biology teacher made it a subject of one of his tangents that he went off on one day. Now, in the interest of fairness, it's not entirely unusual for him to go off on tangents, and if you need an example, look no further than the thorough, thirty-minute explanation of the difference between teaching the reproductive system and sex education. Believe me, I learned some things about Italian state prisons that I did *not* want to know.

But this one took me by surprise. "Stefan, your penmanship is terrible. You need to improve it." Which is teacher-talk for "Your scribbles look like shit." I dunno, he just seemed appalled that I wrote my S's from the bottom up. No matter how hard I tried to tell him that it was a problem deeply rooted in my childhood, he simply ignored me and took the first available flight to triviality, boarding with enough carry-on luggage to make Gallagher's watermelon smashing seem praiseworthy, VH1's presentation of *I Love The '80s* seem amusing, and a laudable explanation of...I'm not sure where I was going with that thought, but I know I didn't get there.

So for an awe-inspiring next five minutes, our class was treated to his interpretive discussion of the ever-increasing importance of being able to compose legible words, and how the way you create your letters reflects your personality and work ethic. It seems that despite your intelligence, production morality, and athletic ability, if you can't write well, you're going to be a failure in life. "They won't accept that in college." Here I was, fairly confident that anything that I would hand in for a college professor would be typed. And then, when I found out that he was telling other classes about how bad my handwriting was, I practically burst my aorta. You know it's bad when the teachers start talking shit about you behind your back.

I distinctly remember another incident where he took a stab at my ego. He was educating us about the human skeletal system, and was using as an example of a gender difference a student of the opposite sex and myself in the class. The idea was that because male hips are slimmer than female, I would, hypothetically, win a foot race between the two of us. At the end of the class, the girl asked whether or not we could really hold a race between she and I during a biology class. His response? "Stefan is too lazy to do that!" I was about to object to such an outrageous slander against my labor standards, when I realized that he was right—I was too lazy.

There always seems to be a big explanation that comes up whenever he starts talking about the Theory of Evolution and its relation to religion. He doesn't want any phone calls from parents, and he's told us that he doesn't on a regular basis. "I'm not sure where evolution is going to take us, and in what way God will play. Maybe he'll wipe out the humans with another flood." WAIT! Wait just one minute! I read some of the Old Testament— He specifically said that He wasn't going to do that again! Haven't you ever read scripture? That was part of the deal with Noah— that the Earth was never again going to be flooded with water like He had just done. And that deal was signed with a rainbow. We still see rainbows from time to time, so from what I can gather, that deal is still in effect. Let's get our facts straight, Mr. "I-Don't-Want-Any-Phone-Calls."

Our biology teacher didn't always captivate us with his creative examples. On the same subject of evolution, he told us the following: "Imagine that we're locked in this room, and that we only get a certain amount of cake per day, and we're each shuffling a deck of cards ..." Longest forty-five minutes of my life. What was really detestable about it was that that particular speech came at a time when my biology class was rotated to last period. We were all set, full of energy, ready to take on the rest of our day, and that spiel just sucked the steam right out of the room. I was yawning so much I thought I was going to have a heart attack. I'd be in the middle of one yawn, and I'd start yawning again, and the whole thing got to the point where I was having trouble breathing.

The quizzes and tests are, hypothetically (as the teacher constantly reminds), easy to pass so long as we study. It isn't always what you would call "effortless" to remember all the information he gives us. Nothing about any of it is exceptionally thrilling. When things are going from humdrum to exceedingly unpalatable, we start pulling every trick in the book, including memory mnemonics (a list of words where the first letter of each word is replaced by another word in a humorous rhyme). There's the ever-popular way to remember the scientific classification system—"King Philip Came Over for Good Spaghetti" (Kingdom, Phylum, Class, Order, Genus, Species); there are also more creative solutions, such as my prize invention: "Oh How Dumb Leprechauns Can't See." And there's Mikey's claim to fame: "Gay Ants Make Boob Butter Fun." Free Pepsi if you can figure out what *that* stands for.

The Metric System: My Other Old Arch-Nemesis

Unintelligible answers to insoluble problems.
— *Henry Brooks Adams*

I never liked any science class for the simple reason of having to use the metric system. I don't care what anybody says or how many people use it; the metric system is a Communist system, plain and simple. I can hardly believe that America is one of only three countries that doesn't use it (the other two being Myanmar in southeast Asia and Liberia in West Africa). For those of you who are looking at me right now like I've grown a third head, I'll take you through it step by step. This subject is just too important for the future of humanity to just blow off. (As always, I take great caution in any sentence in which I use the word "blow.") Here we go:

So, we have this system of numbers based on the number ten (10), which they say is easier because all you have to do is move the decimal point. The problem is, every math teacher and their mother says you should be using fractions because they're easier. Actually, only some of them say that. They alternate each year to throw you off. My pre-algebra teacher told us to use fractions; then next year, my algebra teacher told us to use decimals; then the year after that, my geometry teacher told us to use fractions; and so on. Make no mistake: They're doing it on purpose. Ever wonder what those department chair meetings are for? And those teacher development days? You guessed it—just a cunning cover-up.

The units on the metric system are totally messed up, too. Let's take, for example, oh I don't know, joules. Joules measure kinetic and potential energy. Now, the word "joules" sounds to me like it should measure the quality of gemstones. You know— joules, jewels...makes sense, right? But why would we do something simple like that? No, we measure the quality of gemstones with carats. Personally, I think we should measure the quality of vegetables with carats. Again, the word association just makes sense. So what, then, do we use to measure carrots? Well, we use mass. But mass is not weight. Mass measures how much matter is in a material, which actually makes it sound a lot like volume, but rest assured, the two are completely different.

Like I said, mass is not weight. Nope, the metric equivalent of weight is force, measured in newtons. If you convert pounds (that's weight) to newtons, you're gonna gain a good 700 units on your weight. Or is it mass? Anyway, newtons can measure both how much you weigh and the amount of force that is applied to an object. Let's say we're using newtons to measure the force on an object. That's mass (once again) multiplied by acceleration. Acceleration, by the way, is not how fast you're going; it's how much *faster* you're going. Acceleration is figured out by doing something with the "initial" velocity and the "final" velocity. Velocity does not have anything to do with speed. That would just make way too much sense. No, velocity is a combination of speed and direction. We measure speed in miles per hour. Except metric measures it in kilometers per hour. According to kilometers per hour, you're going about twice as fast. Except you're not going twice as fast, because you're still going the same speed. Or are you still going the same velocity? I suppose that would depend on whether or not you're driving through Pennsylvania.

Back to the joules. In case you've forgotten, joules measure kinetic and potential energy. Suffice to say that potential energy is an interesting concept. It's not how much energy is being spent; it's how much energy *could* be being spent. Isn't that what they say about every child delinquent? "He has potential." I'll bet he has potential, but until he does anything he's just a lazy crackhead. They don't give out Nobel Prizes to "potential" peace talks. Or do they? Hmm …

Joules, being the versatile pieces of crap they are, can also measure something called work. To configure work you multiply force (our old enemy) by distance. If you thought what distance does to velocity was bad, wait to you hear about work. Since there is a distance involved, if you don't actually move something against the force of gravity, you don't do any *scientific* work. For example, if I drag a refrigerator two hundred feet down a hallway, I didn't do any scientific work, despite the fact that I've probably broken a sweat and pulled several muscles. However, if I were to lift that same refrigerator up just one step on my way to the second floor, I've done way, way more scientific work than I did dragging it down the hallway. Which I think just proves that Communists invented it:

"Boris, you didn't do any work today."

"What are you talking about? I was laboring in the factory for fourteen hours!"

"But you didn't do any *scientific* work. No money for you."

That's Communism in a nutshell if I ever saw it. The whole thing is a laugh and a half, and I don't even want to think about what *that* is in metric.

There was always sort of a Communist feel to the class. I'm not saying that I'm calling the teacher a Communist…not officially, anyway. But I should mention one small detail that sticks in my mind. During the sophomore field trip to Washington DC, I was one of the few kids who didn't go (for reasons that I'm still debating to this day). Hence, for three days, my biology class consisted of about three or four students. All of my other classes were just a study hall, but my biology teacher insisted on cramming in a regular class despite there being an insufficient number of students to justify doing so. It was almost as if the motto of the moment was "Efficiency at All Costs." If that's not a line straight out of Marx's manifesto, then I don't know what is.

I guess it's just one of those things that you have to deal with. Like the DMV, or income taxes. So I'll sit back, and enjoy the nonsensical show of big words and funny euphemisms, quietly laughing to myself as I imagine what would happen if the white board were to suddenly burst into flames. I stare into the lights, the noises fade out, I close my eyes and then, "Let's say a kid comes home with a black eye. Now I'm not picking on any ethnic groups, but let's say he's Irish…"

Just five more minutes…Just think: After this class and the next class, and the class after that, and the class after that, and the two classes after that, and the class after that, the day will be over and we'll all get to go home. So we're like…halfway through already.

Miscellaneous Philosophy—Part 2
Life's Great Lessons

There have been a lot of expressions that have the word "life" in them, and I've discovered that I hate every one of them. Usually when I tell someone this, they then say to me, "Hey Stefan! Do you want a LIFEsaver? I don't know, I guess it's just something with the general public and the urge to piss me off. So I started thinking that I should come up with some sayings about life that I approve of. So here they are:

- Life is like a mystery. And Sherlock Holmes is on crack.
- Life is like PBS programming: Even if it's good, you still have to deal with fundraisers.
- Life is like the Green Party: pointless.
- Life is like becoming famous in Oklahoma City: No matter how great your accomplishments, you're still in the middle of nowhere.
- Life is like a bag of cow manure: full of bullshit.
- Life is like a highway: It's important that you pick the right road.

As opposed to someone like me, who picked the wrong road, tried to turn around, missed the exit, tried to ask the guy who didn't speak any English at the 7-11 for directions, had engine problems a few miles after New York City, hitchhiked to the Jersey turnpike, stole somebody's car in a McDonald's parking lot, made the mistake of picking up a hooker who stole my wallet after we did "it" in a Motel 6, accidentally took the Lexington Avenue Express and wound up in Brooklyn, got my mug shot on the ten o'clock news for murdering the guy who didn't speak any English at the 7-11 (American dream, my ass), got addicted to smack, found a guy who could help me out in Harlem, stole another car from a McDonald's parking lot, made it to Cleveland, quit smack by taking up huffing paint thinners, fell into a bad crowd, and got caught up in some kind of riot. The next part is a bit of haze, but when I woke up I found out that it is indeed illegal to hijack a Metro Bus in Canada, snuck back across the border, met up with some old friends in Fargo, got my GED, ran to the nearest pay phone to make a collect call (by dialing down the center, 1-800-C-A-L-L A-T-T) to my hooker girlfriend in Jersey and found out that not only was I wanted in six states but I also had a daughter, "borrowed" a Pepsi truck, made it to Wyoming, took out a loan at the local bank, discovered that the money was counterfeit, shot some people up, fled under the cover of darkness to Colorado, was about to board a plane to Florida, and suddenly realized that I had left my jacket in Cleveland.

So in other words, don't live a life like my car. You might just find yourself out of gas and in the wrong town...and wanted for several felonies.

Chapter Five

The D-Wing Pilgrimage

A route of many roads leading from nowhere to nothing.
—Ambrose Bierce

At last, after what seems like an eternity (though in Terryville, every day feels like an eternity), the bell rings. The bell of freedom rings, releasing us from our hell-bound prison. Now we are free to enter the halls of purgatory, and descend into another hell-bound prison. Downstairs. To U.S. history.

But there's a catch, and there are strings attached. The stairs only go one way. No, it's not an escalator-type deal or anything like that. Our school couldn't even afford to pay someone to begin to think about putting up the pretense of being able to provide something even remotely close to something like that. They, meaning the powers that be (specifically, the system), won't let us go up and down the stairways. There's one stairway where you're allowed to go up, and there's another stairway—at the other end of the school—where you're allowed to go down. Don't like it? Tough luck. School was never designed so you would like it. In fact, ours was designed so that *it* wouldn't like *you* (and that's the *real* reason why it was built in the sixties). Truthfully, there is another "secret" stairway at the far, FAR end of another hallway where you're allowed to go both ways, but that's not really an effervescent innovation. It's more of a newfangled contraption. Just like our elevator. That's "elevator" as in "singular." As in, "We only have one elevator because we're so fucking poor."

Furthermore, biology class (from whence I go forth) is located a stone's throw (which is metric) from the UP stairs, on the second floor. So now, in order to get to U.S. History on the ground floor, you must make a hajj from the biology room to the other end of the second floor hallway, down the DOWN stairs, down the ground floor hallway, then down the secluded hallway to the history room, thereby fully circumnavigating the school. Twice.

When I say the "secluded" hallway, I'm referring to the bleak, murky, clammy corridors of D-Wing, a school extension that was added sometime in the '80s. In keeping with the '80s architecture, the hallway is designed like a bomb shelter, with no direct openings from the classrooms into the antechamber. The bad news is that the lack of direct sunlight gives the passageway a grim, cold feeling that would even make people from the roughest of neighborhoods feel a little uncomfortable. The good news is that if the Soviets were to drop a bomb on us, we would be only mildly incinerated. A quip from a time when we actually sent kids on the roof to see if the Soviets were coming during air raid drills. The time and the hall are one and the same: dark, dismal, and dour. Like the future of humanity when people like me are in charge. There are giant wooden doors that can seal off D-Wing from the rest of the school in case of an emergency. It's a common joke that we'll seal it off in order to keep people from getting out at some point or another. Ironically, most of the freshman homerooms are down that hall.

The best part of all of this is the three minutes passing time that we get in-between classes. Especially considering that from biology to history takes about five. Do you know what our school needs more of? Less people. I kid you not; the halls are like Grand Central Station during rush hour. And yes, I have actually been in Grand Central Station during rush hour. Which is really an oxymoron: it's always rush hour in Grand Central Station. Like the eternal winters of Canada.

If you were to look around during the passing time, you would understand where the inspiration came from for the *Where's Waldo?* books. I once had a teacher who looked a lot like Waldo. That was a weird experience. Especially when he wore a red-and-white striped shirt with blue jeans and showed up late for class. Then it was like *Twilight Zone* weird. "Where's Waldo? That silly jackass is late again!" we'd say. Then you'd notice that he was standing right behind you. Good times. Rod Serling would be proud.

Classroom from Hell...Literally

It requires more courage to suffer than to die.
—Napoleon Bonaparte

The first thing you'll notice as you cross the threshold of the history classroom is a sudden rush of hot air. For some unknown reason, the temperature in this particular chamber is always ten to twenty degrees warmer than anywhere else in the school. I'm not sure if it's because it's located directly above the boiler in the basement, if the torments of the underworld are infused into the walls, or if there's some sort of volcanic vent nearby, but the conditions tend to send your Organs of Rifini into a fritz. My mind harks back to taking the PSATs (the prequel to the SATs, for those who are interested) in that room. The man proctoring the test jokingly asked, "Where else can you get a PSAT and a sauna?"

Hell?

Furthermore, the temperature is always this abnormal, blisteringly hot, even in the summer when the heat shouldn't be on in the first place. I guess no one in school facilities has figured out how to turn it off yet, which, given the intelligence level of the average Terryvillian, is not all that surprising. The assumption of a slightly smarter custodial staff is probably what led to the volcanic vent theory. The best part of all this heat is that it tends to stimulate the already problematic mold issue that has plagued D-Wing for at least a decade, and that doesn't exactly give off a pleasant aroma.

I'll walk into history class as early as possible in order to partake in one of my favorite rituals. I sit at a desk that's on the other side of the room, so as soon as I walk in I throw my back dealie to the other side of the room, aiming for that general area. And when I say (or type) "throw" I don't mean "gently toss." I mean *throw* like I'm slinging the hammer for track and field, probably taking out a few other desks and kids who get in the way. Once I do that, I step up onto the desks and walk across the tops of the desks to the other side of the room before getting down. Why, you ask? Because they didn't let me do it in elementary school, that's why. All those suppressed childhood memories of being yelled at for stupid stuff are coming back (dammit to hell if there wasn't a lot of stupid stuff that I pulled), and now I have issues.

So the class settles down, or at least most of us do, and class starts. I'm not too sure if "start" is the right word for it. "Begins" is probably better. "Start" would imply that there is a definitive point in time at which the class gets underway. To this extent, there isn't one. I've showed up, day-in and day-out, without ever having the feeling that the class genuinely commenced. You'll come in and you'll take notes. You'll come in and take a quiz. You might even come in and take a quiz on those notes you took (assuming that you did indeed take them). But at no point have I ever felt that the class itself had a point, purpose, or was, at any time, going somewhere.

History Is That Wonderful Thing That Constantly Reminds Us That We Messed Up

History repeats itself, first as tragedy, second as farce.
—*Karl Marx*

There was always just something about American history that didn't sit well with me. Then again, I probably didn't sit well with American history. I realize that that is the second time that I've used that joke in this chapter, and I apologize. Things just didn't add up. You read titles at different sections that say things like, "The War Hawks Demand War." Apparently that one just snuck up on us.

All this is not to say that we're not *trying* to learn. We're definitely *trying*. It just seems that at every turn the wheels of history are churning with the best efforts to confound and confuse us. How about a few examples? Let me get out the ol' history book...geez, would you look at all the dust on this thing. Okay, Samuel Slater was a key figure in industrializing America. Wait a minute, wasn't that the guy from *Saved By The Bell*? So not only did he build a major cotton mill in Rhode Island, he also taught Bay Side how to be cool. Admirable. I wonder if Screech was

Secretary of State at some point. Y'know, I, too, have woken up in the morning when the clock has let out a warning thinking that I'd never make it on time.

Then you'll be trying to keep all the Adamses straight, as there was about twenty of those: John Adams, Samuel Adams (like the beer, no relation to John Adams), John Quincy Adams (son of John Adams, no relation to Samuel Adams or the beer), and Douglass Adams (no idea who the fuck that guy is), just to name a few. I won't even get into the Stephen Douglass and Michael Douglass lineup.

How about Matthew Perry, that famous naval commander from the War of 1812? No, that just wouldn't make sense. Why would a naval commander be on *Friends*? I'm guessing, then, that Luke Perry was fighting for the British. Typical, a war tearing families apart. No, wait, that was the Civil War! And they're not related! Son of a bitch!

Back up; when the War Hawks demanded war, they were demanding the War of 1812, right? But if we were fighting the British during the War of 1812, then why would there be war with the Native Americ—(furiously turning pages)—aww, dammit to hell! The War Hawks weren't Indians! They were congressmen! Okay, where is that section on the wars we had with the Indians? I know we had several...(more page turning). Geez, we were at war with Spain, too? It says right here: "King Philip's War." Wait, King Philip wasn't a king of Spain. Well, he *was*, but it seems that *this* King Philip was an Indian! So the Indians were congressmen and the European kings were the Indians. I guess that makes European kings our congressmen. That's enough chaos to make your colon knot. So what the hell was the Pope doing in southwestern America? Oh wait, my bad, that doesn't say "Pope," that says "Popé." It seems that Popé (notice the accent mark) was another Indian leader. Holy shit! These Indians are everywhere! No wonder we shot them all. Well, most of them, anyway. Apparently some survived and built casinos.

Didn't we have any *real* Indian leader names? (Quick flip to the index.) Okay, here we go: There was a Little Turtle, no relation to the Battle of Little Big Horn; and there was a Sioux chieftain named Sitting Bull, no relation to the Cherokee chieftain, Squatting Bear. Well, that's just stupid; why would an Indian chieftain be taking a shit in a Jeep Grand Cherokee? So it says here that we beat Little Turtle at the Battle of Fallen Timbers.

Who comes up with the names for all these battles, anyway? I remember that there was a Battle of Tippecanoe, and I thought, "Tip the canoe? We'll never win that way! Just shoot some Injuns, white boy!" Seriously, though, some of them are obvious. Like the battle that took place on Lake Erie was called the Battle of Lake Erie (which we won, by the way). But some of these others don't even make sense. Trafalgar? That's not a word! Why even put the "r" on the end if it's going to be silent? It was near the Strait of Gibraltar; why not call it the Battle of Gibraltar? Then there's the Battle of Bunker Hill. Except for the simple fact that we weren't fighting on Bunker Hill at all, we were fighting on Breed's Hill. No wonder we lost; we were fighting on the wrong fuckin' hill! Saratoga was the turning point in the war? The hell it wasn't! The last I checked, there wasn't anything of any strategic value in upstate New York. There still isn't. And of course we won—the troops were Canadian.

Do the generals sit around in their command tent before the campaign coming up with these things?

"If we win, I think we should call it 'The Battle of Victory Falls,' but if we lose, Bob proposes that we call it 'The Battle Where We Fucked Up Falls.'"

Another general chimes in: "What the hell does Bob know? The only reason why he's a general is because his cousin is in cahoots with King Philip. No, asshole! The *other* King Philip! I say we call it 'The Battle of Victory Garden.' Who knows? One day we might even get our own series!"

Wait a minute...*Victory Garden* is on Home and Gardening Television, not the History channel! And the term "victory garden" comes from American propaganda during the Second World War! Oh, fuck this shit ...

World History Was Insane
(and So Was the Teacher)

People are more easily led than driven.
—*David Harold Fink*

At least all of this American history isn't nearly as bad as world history was last year. That class was so bad, you could almost hear Buddha laughing at us from above. I remember walking into the world history room, which is only a little ways down from the U.S. history room, and immediately you'd feel this rush of broiling hot air. What is this? Why are all the history rooms in this school reminiscent of the Sahara Desert? Believe me, it didn't matter that it was a dry heat. The curriculum was especially annoying since unlike American history, I did have a lot background information about what was going on in the rest of the world. Despite this, the class had to be dumbed-down for the rest of the students who seemed to have trouble figuring out anything. I remember on the first day, when the teacher asked if there were any questions, someone (no names now, no names) asked, "So, like, were the cavemen around during the time of the dinosaurs?"

I quietly shook my head, then looked to the sky and said, "What the hell are you laughing at?" I was pretty sure that all of us, every single last one of us, had learned this fact at some point in the last five years. I've known that the dinosaurs died out before the humans since I was seven. I can even give you a number: sixty-five million. The last dinosaurs died out sixty-five million years *before* humans. Of course, I then made fun of that particular student whenever possible for a long time to come. "Jen, how stupid can you be?!" was my battle cry, as if in a melodramatic reproduction of Shakespeare's *The Tragedy of Julius Caesar*, I, like Octavious—"Draw my sword against idiocy!" Oh wait, that was "conspirators." Just think: English class is just over the horizon. That was always a funning saying. Why does everyone always think that whatever is over the horizon is something good? For all you know, impending doom could be over the horizon. It never struck you as odd that all those sunrises were a burning shade of red?

What about Jen, this girl who challenged me on the anti-Amnesty International crusade, pestered me at every opportunity, and drove the computed average intelligence of everyone in the room through the floor? There's not much to say about Jen. Correction—there's not much good to say about Jen. She was a shapely brunette whom you might have found foxy to some extent. That is, until you had so much as a five-minute conversation with her. Born with a suck-up chromosome firmly lodged in her genetic makeup, she was loud, obnoxious, annoying, feeble-minded, incompetent, dimwitted, bitchy, and would never, ever, *ever* stop talking. At times it would seem that she was going out of her way just to piss me off (as well as those around her).

It's one of those classic rivalries. She tells me that I have psychotic anger problems; I tell her she has bitch problems. She tells me to shut up; I tell her to get the fuck out of my face. She hits me several times in the arm; I try to stab her with my pen; and things just kind of escalate from there. For the past six years, she has been in my classes. Fate certainly has a sick, twisted sense of humor. This year, I almost missed her. Almost. *Almost, dammit!* History is the only class that we have together, and sure enough, no week is free from a circumstance where we aren't at each other's throats. Everyone looks on laughing. They're always laughing. At everything. My anger and suffering is like the national past time for them. Bastards. Maybe I'm just desperate for attention.

But that wasn't even the worst that world history had to offer. Oh no, my friend, it gets worse. Take for example, our second semester "mini" research paper. This "mini" research paper, as it just so happened, had to be five pages long. I don't know about you, but to me the word "mini" implies something in the neighborhood of a short paragraph that requires the research equivalent of a quick click on the Google directory. The report itself was on that eternal question that has been plaguing historians and analysts for centuries: Were the crusades a success or a failure? Oh, wait a minute, that question isn't a paradoxical incertitude— it's an expedition into the vast underworld of stupidity! This question hasn't plagued anyone, *ever*! Yeah, after all, the three things that I think about right before I go to sleep every night are the future of the American economy, the violence in the Middle East...and whether or not Europeans marching on Jerusalem eight hundred years ago was a faux pas.

It seems so absurdly simple on the surface. The crusades were a success in the sense that they encouraged people to travel more, strengthened the power of the Catholic church (briefly), and opened up Europe to the rest of the world, thereby flooding it with all sorts of new goods and thus hastening the decline of the Middle Ages. Simple: Crusades = good. It's a standard, straight-out-of-the-book answer. There's just one small stipulation to the report—hindsight cannot be used at all. Now we hit a wall, because everything that we know about the crusades comes from using hindsight. If you don't use hindsight, then the crusades were an abominable failure. We won't get into the contradiction that the history teacher is now teaching us something that is the opposite of what actually happened, because my doctor tells me that my blood pressure can only go so high.

The report was assigned two months before it was due. So I sat down on the Saturday of the weekend before the Monday that it had to be turned in. Why? Like I said before, that's just how I operate. I was logging on to the Internet to do some research, when a horrible realization came to mind: Our world history teacher had clearly pointed out to us that only *original* sources could be used. This ruled out any book, magazine, web site, newspaper, or other publication that was written *about* the crusades *after* the crusades. Where was I going to find information now? Well, we'd have to look into a speech made by the Pope of the time, accounting books kept by the Knights Templar, and— my personal favorite—Jalalabad's personal dairy of the crusading expeditions. Y'know, for an objective Arabic point of view.

All of this led to my one true work-cited source for every report—the bullshit. Ah yes, if you can't dazzle them with information, baffle them with bull. With a renewed sense of purpose to try to put my best effort into giving up, I finished all five pages of it in just under seven hours, work cited and all. After running it through spell-check, I then read through it to make sure that it had all of the following elements:

• lengthy, in-depth descriptions about absolutely nothing;

- the following key words: crusades, dissonance, repro-
  bate, and cessation;
- at least two paragraphs that make the twelfth-century
  Pope look like a jackass;
- and, most importantly, at least three sentences that begin
  with the letter "K."

That's all it takes, really. SAVE. PRINT. Good job.

The next night (the night before it was due), I got a phone call. It was one of my illustrious fellow classmates. Actually, it was a chain call of about four or five of my illustrious fellow classmates. Fascinatingly, in a matter of only a few short hours they had set up a network of people—each running multiple computers—that was efficiently and effectively gathering every fact and figure that was even remotely related to the crusades, every possible detail from how much funding was required from the Holy Roman Empire to Sultan Saladin's mother's favorite dinner. (All I remember was that it wasn't pork.) So I gave the network several invaluable URL addresses, which were then e-mailed to the rest of Litchfield County. On several occasions during that week, many students repeatedly thanked me, most of whom I had never met before. But that's what this whole report was about—bringing people together in a time of crisis. Why? What did you think it was? It sure as hell wasn't to learn something.

At the end of such a lengthy story about something that means so extraordinarily little in the big scheme of things, we're left with one burning question on all of our minds: What did I get on this hell-sent project? And if that's not the question on your mind, just play along. Well, after all that long suffering and bitching, I received a well-earned 85. Considering that the class average for the paper was something like 73, I felt like I had accomplished something for once. Yes, just once. Seeing how poorly most of the class did, and the overwhelming number of people who failed, our history teacher generously offered (insert sarcasm *HERE*) to let us rewrite the paper, and then average the new grade with the old grade.

Rewrite it? We didn't know what the fuck we were doing the first time! I remember one student (no names now, no names) who wrote his paper had the teacher look over it and correct it, stayed after school and rewrote it, had the teacher look over it and correct it again, and then took it home and rewrote it yet again. His grade? A mere 77. Being the smart-ass that I am, I ran my paper through spell-check again, changed a few words, and handed it right back in. Hey, it brought my grade up to a clean 86. Pretty damn good, if you ask me. Who would have thought that indifference was the key to success? And you, kindly reader, foolishly thought that it was hard work and perseverance. There's an old Southern proverb: "The slave who puts in a hard day's work and perseveres gets nothing but slavery in return. The slave who gives up and runs away gains freedom." Now that I think about it, that's not a Southern proverb, that's my proverb. And it's a pretty damn good proverb at that.

Ultimately, the grief and pain of the whole experience was soon forgotten. Our freshmen history experience passed us just as quickly as it came, though some said not nearly quick enough. As much as time continues on to point B, we continued on to U.S. history, where at this very moment I sit, suffering with contempt.

All Work and No Learning Makes a History Class

From time to time, historians need to be shocked.
—Peter Burke

The total crap factor of U.S. history classes aside, I do enjoy the people that I've got in the room suffering with me. If nothing else, it's good people. Behind me is Mikey. His name is Mike and we all call him Mike, but I'll use "Mikey" in order to distinguish him from the aforementioned Mike from the bus, as there are many Mikes in my school. Mikey is the educational comic relief, and will undoubtedly be in direct competition with me for the "Class Clown" accolades come our senior year. A dark haired, stalwart man of character, his personality is almost always seemingly bubbling over with energy and charisma. He's nothing short of a musical genius on drums, guitar, and keyboard, and a stellar baseball and soccer player, not to mention his remarkable knack for drawing.

In other words, he's everything that I'm not. He's the only person I've ever known who has taken days off simply to play video games, usually Tuesdays and Thursdays. Those aren't his official days, just the ones that seem to fit the pattern. He's berated me in the past for my criticism of his modest slacker lifestyle. Example? Biology quiz bonus question: In what city of Spain did the terrorist train bombings take place? Then, moments later, this exchange, initiated by Mikey:

"I knew the answer to that one! I saw it on *CNN Headlines*."

"Yeah, well, I'd be able to watch the news, too, if I took two days off from school every week!"

"Shuddup, Stefan!"

All the ladies seem to be clamoring after him, as evidenced by his twenty-something ex-girlfriends (again, that's quantity, not age). Then again, most of the ladies are unmistakably bitches and hos. Take it as you will.

Then, to my right, is Serena. Standing at about five foot three on account of the constant presence of heeled shoes, she alternates between illogical sanguinity and perpetual pessimism. An animal-lover at heart, her long, swarthy brown hair often covers the features of her regularly unsmiling face. Well, on some days she smiles, at certain people. Her smile is of the warm, cozy, everything-is-okay variety. Her frowns, on the other hand, are of the dark, maniacal, I'm-about-to-summon-demons-from-Hell type. On most days, she's shrouded in stark stillness, her tenebrous eyes observing every movement, her thoughts a downright enigma. If you can catch her on a good day, you'll be able to see a much more lighthearted side, one that is filled with a great deal of childlike wonder and ease. I guess that the optimum way to describe her would be a delinquent image, covering a sweet-mannered interior, covering a downcast inner-self—if that makes any sense to you. With her bronzed coloration (Italian by origin, tanning booth by trade) and her thinly curved frame, any guy would likely find her devilishly attractive. That is, if she didn't utterly freak you out first.

I recollect that when I first met her in eighth grade, I was looking at the cover of her organizer, on which the word "Xambola" was printed in inky black lettering. When she noticed me staring at it, she said to me in the most dulcet, amiable voice imaginable, "It says 'Xambola'—it means 'Gateway to Hell.'" I consider myself lucky to be someone who doesn't often judge, because there's frequently a large contingent of fabricators who would look at her—with her not-so-loose shirts, her few noticeable piercings (through the eyebrow, tongue, bellybutton, and a multitude in both ears)—and would then look at the people she associates with, and would immediately reach the conclusion that she's bad news. If there's one thing that I've learned about high school, it's that you can't trust anyone—not even people who are on your side from the start. I'm not sure whom to believe sometimes. Serena, being the only person who has ever considered me normal, is probably the one who keeps me bolted to reality and reality bolted to me. I'd thank her for that, but I doubt she would have any clue as to what I was talking about. I'd say she's okay, but I really don't know that much about her. Then again, maybe it's more than I think.

Like Mikey, she's also a talented artist, though she would never in a million years join a sports team. I've always admired people with the ability to draw well, probably due to the fact that I'm so disturbingly awful at it. A pity too, because unlike other things, an artistic gene runs through my family. I have it, too, but...you know how an ostrich has wings, but they're so underdeveloped that they can't fly? That's what I have. I have an underdeveloped artistic gene. I'm "art retarded." Serena is about as smart in history as I am skilled in art. It is her Achilles heel, if you will.

Behind Serena is Dan. Forever questing and forever questioning Dan. One of the few other kids in the school who has his piceous hair spiked in a manner somewhat similar to mine, he is one of your standard inquisitive individuals. Every day holds a new search for obscure knowledge, without any real connection between topics from one day to the next. He sank himself a little too deep with drugs and drinking this year than he would have liked. He was unremittingly asking me about the effects of different narcotics, because I guess I look smart or something. He wanted to know how many brain cells were killed per puff of marijuana. How was I supposed to know something like that? When he tried to get off it, he started experimenting with some pretty unusual alternatives. He wanted to know all the effects of those, too. One day, as he came in with a story of his latest escapade, he was telling me, "I took one hit off of it, but it wasn't even a drug."

Skeptical as always, I tried to explain something to him: "Dan, if you took a 'hit' off of it, then it was a drug…I don't take hits off of hamburgers, and therefore, hamburgers are not drugs." My excuse for not getting started on drugs is because I never fell into that crowd. I'm not sure what I mean by that, but it's as good an excuse as any.

For all the fields that Dan is slipping in, though, there is one thing that Dan and I have in common: We both share a common dream. We both share the desire to become something more than what we are, and the yearning to make something of ourselves in this world. When he finally gets around to taking a break from his drug talk and conversations about how much he hates school/teachers/people, he asks me about my films, video projects, scripts, and books. He's betting on the band that he's in to take him where he wants to go in life, along with several others. Quite frankly, I'm not sure if any of us are going to reach the lofty goals that we have set for ourselves, but when you grow up in a small town like Terryville, it's something that you can't help but hope for.

These people are so good in history that I don't even sit facing forward most of the time. I sit sideways at my desk, facing toward Serena with Mikey on my right (and to his right is Dan). It just makes the subject matter that much more entertaining. Not that it's the subject matter that I'm legitimately giving any heed to.

While I'm enjoying the company of my fellow schoolmates, the teacher will get up to the front of the room and start talking. There's nothing that she says that's really worth mentioning here, but suffice to say that the majority of her spiels end with the entire class moaning. And I don't mean that in a good way.

Soon we see why, as a ditto or two is passed back from person to person in the each of the columns of desks. The dittos themselves aren't too overwhelmingly difficult. However, there are always five to ten extra questions that the slave driv—I mean, "educator"—will have us add to the back of the paper. Serena usually takes one look at the assignment before asking me, "Can

I get this from you tomorrow?" I always tell her yes. The two of us are constantly going back and forth, trading homework from one subject or another. I guess that would make us cheat-pals (cooperative education partners). Take it as you will. She goes back to toiling on the English homework that she's been working on since the class started. I've seen her version of studying for history tests. She takes a garden variety of cheat-sheets (convenience sheets) and lodges them in her belt, like Batman about to go on a mission. She takes the situation very seriously—three kids have already been caught cheating (cooperatively learning) in this class already.

Josh is also among those in desperate need of history homework help. A lot of other people are as well, but they usually refrain from asking me for aid. Some because they don't want to risk feeling stupid as a result (as self-esteem always comes before grades), but mostly because my handwriting is largely indecipherable (though no teacher, save in biology, has complained as of yet). They told us while we were in late elementary that we had to learn cursive, and that once you got to high school they wouldn't accept anything else. It was bullshit. They lied to us. Again. I, however, got hooked on it, and now I can't even write in print if I want to. Nevertheless, Josh is what you would call a skeptical optimist. He's a bright-eyed, high-flying, easy-laughing individual. He'll at least look at it before he gives up. Serena doesn't care enough to try to get correct answers. All she wants is to get through this thing with her average relatively intact. And Dan...Dan will take bets as to what his grade is going to be. Mikey always guesses high, I always guess low, and Dan goes somewhere in between. Oddly enough, Mikey has won the last two.

I don't blame anyone for not being able to read my history notes. They aren't nearly as important to me as biology notes. In biology, it is crucial that I understand what I've written. In history, not so much. Because of that, I take a lot of short cuts and often wind up abbreviating random words. The following is an excerpt from my history notes on the American war with Mexico in the 1840s:

ORIGINAL—"SA leads Mex into Tex and A's the A in NA. The NA's don't like SA in NA, and SH leads Tex and A's SA's Mex. SH beats SA after A & G. A—W TG Tex-Mex AS? "

TRANSLATION—"Santa Anna leads the Mexican army into Texas and attacks the Alamo in North America. The Native Americans don't like Santa Anna in North America, and Sam Houston leads the Texan army in an attack against Santa Anna's Mexican army. Sam Houston defeats Santa Anna after the battles he won at the Alamo and Goliad. Anybody want to get Tex-Mex after school?

The spiel and the ditto-passing together only take up about five minutes. What do we do for the rest of the forty minutes left in the period? Work on that ditto, of course. Then tomorrow we'll go over and correct the ditto. Then the day after that, we'll get another ditto. At some point we'll get a quiz or a test on all those dittos we did. As is fairly evident by now, there is no real class, no real teaching, no real learning. Taken all together, there's no real education. Just a room full of kids and a copy machine. The rest is frivolous window-dressing. Different teachers have different standards. Our biology teacher gets our papers back to us within the period; our history teacher has trouble getting our papers back within the month. It's like FedEx versus the Italian postal service (which to this day delivers mail via bicycle).

Occasionally, we get a real treat: one of those wonderfully made educational videos that are not only edifying, but pleasantly amusing, too! Yeah, brainwashing is more like it. These things are so bad, they make *Sesame Street* look like it should get a Golden Globe nomination. The kind of actors and actresses who are readily abundant in these slipshod tapes would leave you to believe that the company was producing it with a fifty-dollar budget in mind. The soundtrack is dreadful at best, and at worst it's an excursion into the arid underworld of Philharmonic Hell. The decades-old recordings blast tunes that embody a bizarre mix of war documentary and *Andy Griffith Show* episode. The sleep-inducing dialogue is comparable to taking NyQuil, except without the nasal-congestion relief. I hope they have some kind of warning label on the box cover about watching the video and then driving or operating heaving machinery, or they could get their asses sued.

On a good day, or perhaps I should say a good week, we'll get to watch a real movie. After we went over the Revolutionary War, we got to watch *The Patriot* (after getting a permission slip signed). For a movie where you already knew the ending, it was pretty well done. The only part that I didn't get was when Gibson's son is about to kill that guy, and he takes what seems like five minutes to stab him and winds up getting stabbed himself. Honestly, how long does it take to decide to stab someone? Let's see, I'll time myself: There's that guy...I'm going to stab him...STAB! Okay, I counted six seconds.

But in the film, it seems to take forever. It was almost as if his train-of-thought was: "There's that guy...I really don't like him...I mean, I'm sure he's a nice guy and all...we'd probably get along really well if we got to know each other...well, better get this over with...First I'll position myself over him...where the hell's my stabbing knife? Oh, here it is...I suppose the best way to do this is to raise this knife thing over my head and then bring it down on him...Okay, here it goes...I'll just raise it above my head...higher...a little bit higher...that's good...I wonder if he has any kids? I'd feel just terrible about killing their father...ah, well, such is war...I'll just exhale deeply for good measure...alright, I'm gonna do this...right now! STAB!...Shit, I'm dying!...This sucks...eyes closing...light fading...and I never got a chance to come out of the closet ..."

Yeah, that was about five minutes or so. I like to think that that's nature's way of weeding out the stupid people. And then it takes even longer for him to die! Long enough for Gibson to ride over, slowly bend down, and then have a ten-minute, teatime death discussion.

Several months later, we were treated to another cinematic thrill. We watched *Amistad* (after getting a permission slip signed). Y'know how it seems that either Morgan Freedman or Steven Spielberg are somehow associated in some way with every movie made in the past seven years? Well, this one has both! There's some pretty brutal brutality in that thing. When one of the slaves is getting whipped, you could hear the entire class going, "Oooh..." usually followed by a not-so-clever cliché, like, "That's GOT TA HURT!" or "He's gonna feel that one in the morning!" Well, I guess I was the one who was making most of the inappropriate sidebar comments; me and that kid in the back corner of the room who was constantly shouting, "Die, y'damn Negroes!" He didn't use the word "Negroes," but if this book is an example of anything, it's that I'm a writer with a sense of ethics. It's still not as bad as what someone said in one of the other classes at a scene (from another movie) in which hundreds of dead African American soldiers were sprawled out across a beach after a major battle: "Look at those Negroes! They're trying to get a tan!" Ouch.

And that last line in the movie by that British naval commander? Classic. Not laugh-out-loud funny, but something that would inspire a hardy British chuckle. Especially if you've actually been to Sierra Leone—rough neighborhood. The capital city is called "Freetown"? Wow, they must have been up all night thinking of that one. Just like Newfoundland, or, in other words, New-found-land. The Vikings were many great things, but thinking up names was obviously not their forte. (Iceland, Greenland, Vinland...Pattern, perhaps?)

Then there was the video about the Alamo. Interestingly enough, the siege of this historic landmark lasted twelve days. Why? Because the general of the Mexicans, Santa Anna, was waiting for his eighteen-pound cannon to arrive so he could blast through the walls. Equally interesting was that the video went through the siege day-by-day. So you can imagine what that must have been like:

Day 1—We have fortified ourselves around the Alamo. We await the arrival of our eighteen-pound cannon so that we may begin the assault.
Day 2—We are still awaiting the arrival of that cannon.
Day 3—I asked Lieutenant Paco as to when the cannon might be arriving. He said he didn't have the slightest clue.
Day 4—Still waiting for the cannon.
Day 5—Where the hell is that thing?
Day 6—Son of a bitch! Where the fuck is that cannon?!
Day 7—Dammit to hell! I want my cannon!
Day 8—FUCK!
Day 9—Several men were shot at today. We still have no idea where that cannon is.

Day 10—My patience is starting to wear thin. Supplies are good, ammunition is plentiful, but do you know what would be great? A CANNON, DAMMIT!

Day 11—I have decided to cut off Lieutenant Paco's head, so that I may fire it from the cannon when it arrives.

Day 12—Oh, fuck this shit! I'm gonna attack that damn fort without the cannon.

The cannon never arrived. He conquered the Alamo in less than an hour later that night.

Most of the time, though, it's just the same old work. The lessons all sort of run together after awhile. Someone got mad, we had a war, we won. Someone got mad, we had a war, we won. Right down the line—Indians, British, French, Indians again, British again, Mexicans, ourselves, Indians a third time, Germans, Japanese, Germans again, Koreans, Vietcong (a tie), Iraq, Afghanistan, Iraq again. The rest is just details, which take up the rest of the two years of American history. Same old same-old.

With the present thoughts of the past, I scribble down data that has long since been forgotten by the majority of Americans, pausing every now and then to stare at the clock, quietly laughing to myself as I imagine what would happen if it were to suddenly burst into flames. The music quietly playing in the back of my head helps make the work go faster. Wait a minute, that music isn't playing in my head—it's coming from another classroom. Oh well, you've got to go with what you've got. Sing along, everyone: "I'm a rocket man. Rocket man burning out his fuse up here alone…"

If you ever felt like it was a waste of time, speak now or forever shut up. And while I'm on that thought, have you ever said to your history teacher, "Do you know what you and Napoleon Bonaparte have in common?" and when he asks, "What?" you say "*Your mother!*"

I wouldn't recommend it.

Miscellaneous Philosophy—Part 3
Surplus Time Hazards

Think outside the box?
We ARE the box.

I ran into a bit of a puzzler when going for my afternoon snack yesterday. I reach for the bottle of Pringles, and the top of the box (or tube, I guess you would call it) reads "Made in USA!" Well, that's nice, but the thing was that the side of the bottle was in Spanish, proudly declaring that these new Pringles were "Con Grasa Reduca! (With Reduced Fat!)" What kind of message is that sending?

Got a problem? Take a drug!

One of the big dilemmas that I ran into while writing this book was the issue of semicolons—when and how often they should be used. I'm not sure if I even like them. It's as if someone was writing a sentence and couldn't decide if they wanted to use a comma or a period, so they used both.

Several nights ago, I was doing my English homework, and to my astonishment, jig, jigger, jiggle, jim crow, jim-dandy, and jingoism are all real words.

I was watching a Spanish news show once, and what they were showing were mass riots, public uprisings and unrest, violent demonstrators, and a plethora of special ops forces mercilessly beating back the crowd. So in other words, it was just another Monday in Bolivia. Don't you just hate Mondays?

The Ultimate Parting Shot:
Gay is to Fag, Fag is to Gaf, Gaf is to Giraffe—You're Ugly.
(Courtesy of Serena and her friend, Cait.)

"Reach for the stars"...I don't like that phrase. The farther you reach, the more likely you're going to crash down on yourself. Now, "shoot for the moon"...I like that one. You get a shotgun out, and we can shoot for the moon all night.

Chapter Six

After that enthralling historical ordeal, it's time to depart from the D-Wing portal. As I round the corner of the passageway, I can already see the light emitting from the outside school world. Yes, the light...head toward the light...head towards the liiiiiiiiii-iight. Out we are, safe, if not sound. As we approach the only four-way intersection in the entire school, we have to make a decision as to whether to swing left or right. Straight leads out of the school into the outside, otherwise noted as the real world. As much as we would like to go straight, we have to swing either left or right. Most of us will swing right, but since we need to head to the boys' locker room for gym, we'll have to swing left. There aren't a lot of benefits to swinging left, but it's something that we all have to do sooner or later. I'm not sure if all that was a political metaphor or a gay pun. I think I might have just gotten carried away.

Heigh-Ho, Heigh-Ho, It's Off to Personal Health and Fitness We Go!

We choose our joys and sorrows long before we experience them.
—Kahlil Gibran

We—as we are all in this together—open one door and then another that leads into the boys' locker room. No matter what you do, no matter what time of day, no matter what, the locker room smells like ass. Unless you go in right after the janitors have "cleaned" it—then it smells like lemony ass. Tasty. There are showers in our locker room, but given that I don't so much as trust drinking the water in this school, what the hell makes you think that I'm going to bathe in it? Besides, I don't have school health insurance.

Your standard T-shirt and shorts work fine for me. I lace up a black pair of ordinary sneakers, silently wondering how these things have lasted since seventh grade, never mind the fact that they still fit me. What are the odds? Pretty good, considering it's happening now. Enough small talk; we're here to play some high-quality Terryville gym! The administration doesn't call it "gym" anymore. The keen minds behind such classical terms as "pharmaceutical enthusiast" (druggie) and "educationally deficient" (stupid) now present their newest creation: "Personal Health and Fitness Class." You clever, clever bastards.

Filing out into a small, dimly lit gateway, we proceed into a vast, expansive gym. Our only gymnasium is the biggest thing in our school. It serves as both gym and auditorium, with the stage right on the borders of the basketball out-of-bounds line. The numerous scuff-marks, surface scratches, and paint peelings are enough to make you sigh in disgust. It's so bad, it has character.

For some of us, such as the likes of Mike and Mikey, gym is the one and only good part of the day (other than lunch). As you might expect, then, they put a lot of heart, intensity, effort, and determination into anything that we play. Which makes the games all that much more interesting. A few quick laps, several stretches, push-ups, and sit-ups, and we're ready to go. The stretching and the laps are probably the most useful parts of the warm up. The sit-ups and push-ups are in preparation for the physical fitness test, which most of us passed but have to put up with because of the No Child Left Behind Act. I hate to go off on tangents—even though this whole book may seem like a tangent at times—but this thing is something that I must bring attention to.

No Child Left Behind was enacted in order to, well, it's pretty obvious what it's supposed to do. One of the components of this written law is to require high school students to pass a test in order to get out of high school. For people like me, who have a somewhat decent amount of intelligence, the test is no problem. However, for students of lower intelligence, who don't have a snowball's chance in Hell of passing, the test is considerably more difficult. Hence, they will not make it out of high school. In our efforts to leave no child behind, we have now started to leave children behind.

I bring it up because our Personal Health and Fitness instructor, Mr. Sckonz, finds the whole situation quite humorous. Right around our fiftieth push-up, he'll start saying things like, "Come on, guys! I want you to look at me and smile, and say, 'Thank you Mr. Sckonz, for not leaving me behind!'"

Thanks Mr. Sckonz! Fuck you state legislation! The push-ups aren't really as bad as the sit-ups, which have more positions than most conventional types of sex. After twenty-five of those in twenty-something positions, Mr. Sckonz enthusiastically tells us, "Alright! We're going to try something different now!"

Mike pipes up, "What?! We're still not done?! Jesus Christ!"

Sckonz chuckles and replies to Mike's inexplicable burst of religion with, "That's the right person to be calling on!" Low standards always produce some amazing results.

Prison Ball

I don't know if this is an official sport or not, but if it isn't, it definitely should be. The classic rules that have been used for generations still apply. The object of the game is to hit someone with bouncy balls that contain an abnormally high level of elasticity. If you get hit, you have to go to prison (located behind the basketball baselines). If the person you throw the ball at catches it, you have to go to prison. Once in prison, the only way to get out is to have one of your remaining team members throw the ball over the heads of the enemy and into the prison, where you then have to catch it. If you catch it, you pass the ball off to the enemy as you return to your side. (I bring it up only because some have grown up with "prison ball," and others with "dodge ball.") It's all so simple. So completely simple, and yet so infinitely exciting.

At this point, I'm sure that not all of you are on the same wavelength as I am when I talk about the game of prison ball. There is so much more depth to it than what you can see on the surface. It's more than basic ball-passing, and it's so much more than the piece-of-shit court cases saying that the game is unfair to kids who are not athletically gifted. Because every sport is. Sports are a simulation of nature, and just like in nature, the slow, the fat, and the stupid are eliminated fairly quickly. You may not like the truth, but that doesn't make it false. A somewhat biased opinion, since I was never one of the slow, fat, or stupid…well, definitely not slow or fat.

Every time you play this momentous game, you are living an alternate reality. The most commonly used analogy is that of a war zone. The court is transformed into a battlefield. Suddenly, you are plunged into a combat situation unlike any other. A chance to experience something totally outside of what we're used to. Like DOOM on God mode. We get the opportunity to imagine ourselves in the different roles that we would, under normal circumstances, never take up in real life.

Perhaps we picture ourselves as the upcoming private, the newly recruited foot soldier—charging the front lines to take a few potshots at the enemy before ducking down into the trenches. Staunch allies to the end, supplying our friends with ammunition, and dying alongside them as we start taking round after round of flak under near-impossible odds. The fearless warrior of the engagement, we are the pride and joy of any prison ball team.

Or perhaps we are the artillery officer behind the lines, grimly overlooking the current situation with a strategic eye. Walking the back lines, we arm the weaponry, look through the binoculars to make the last few critical calculations, and then fire an onslaught of projectiles high into the air. Our opponents take one quick look of horror before making the decision to hit the deck. The echoes of explosions and screams resonant in our ears, and the men on the frontlines nod a sign of gratitude in our direction. After a small swelling of pride, we prepare the next round.

Or perhaps we are the more sly and devious type, in which case we might be the sharpshooter, slinking along the sidelines. Always searching for the few key small bouncy balls, the ones necessary for a quick, precise hit. We find one, probably no bigger than six inches in diameter—perfect. Making haste, we move as far forward as we can without being noticed. Scanning the enemy formation, we look for someone to pick off. The best people are those who have just thrown their own ball, since there is always a pause (a few seconds in length) to see whether it hits someone or if they catch it, and of course, always those who stand completely unaware of their impending downfall. We find that one kid who is standing dangerously close to the gym halfway line, entertaining himself with the foolish thought of his invincibility. Target sighted.

Clutching the ball—our hands profusely perspiring with the sweat of anticipation—and murmuring a small wish for good luck, our arm makes a swift overhand cut with the most strength our biceps can muster. When the energy is at its maximum and the timing is just right, we release our ever-so-tense grip and send the body-bound bullet hurtling through the air. BAM! Direct hit! Our foe looks with utter dismay as the full reality of what has just happened hits him mere moments after the ball has. Fists clenched, he looks around to try to spot the one who has taken him down. All he sees is our smiling face as we slink back into the crowd of troops.

Or perhaps we are the cruel and unforgiving type, in which case we might find ourselves guarding the prison, ceaselessly pacing back and forth along the lockup line whilst the multitudes of captives cry to the other members of their team to free them from the intolerable Bastille. Our prying eyes spot someone on the opposite side sending a ball soaring into the air in order to try to get one of the malefactors free. Making a quick judgment as to the ball's trajectory, we dash down the line. As it starts losing altitude, the other detainees anxiously shout, "Catch it! Catch it!" But before they get the chance to, we leap into the air and catch it in mid-flight. They shall not be liberated while we're on duty. With this thought, we beam a sinister grin of evil satisfaction.

There is also the chance that we might be the uninterested and unmotivated person who stands near the back and doesn't do anything. Although these people do exist, I found it exceedingly difficult to think of what these people would be in an approximated real-life situation. While I thank them for being part of the team, I'm afraid I'll have to leave them out of the metaphoric explanation.

For those of you who are doubting my sanity (and if you haven't already, I don't know why the hell you would start now), I would like to take this unique opportunity to describe to you a chronicle of competition, if you will, of what happened during several prison ball games collectively and filled with all the standard drama and vicissitudes that you might expect from an old war story. Gather 'round, little ones, and I shall tell you a tale...

All Is Not So Quiet on the Western Front

There is nothing more exhilarating than to be shot at without result.

—Winston Churchill

The teams have been decided. All of the selections are final. To each his own has decided whom he will fight for. Some go to one side, the others to the opposite side. Across the gym we stare at each other, our eyes filled with anxiety, excitement, and an ever-so-small desire for swift and ruthless action. Ever so small. All of the "ammunition" is lined up along the black line that divides the gym neatly into two equal halves, two equal fields. The competitors line up at the far ends of the gymnasium. At the given command, both will race toward the center to be the first to grab a ball and throw it at someone. Runners seek out competition, lining up opposite each other to match one another's capabilities. The fastest of the fastest focus their minds, their steely gazes set firmly on the buckshot they're going for. Everything is set, and our ears attentively listen for that one command that will begin the blitzkrieg.

Sckonz's voice breaks the spectral, dead air: "Alright! *Let's play!*"

In an instant, twenty or so young, athletically toned humans dash toward one another at breakneck speeds. I am among them, near the front of the rush. Though I am one of the faster kids in the class—if not the fastest for short distances—I have pre-planned my position so that I am up against one of the slower members. Call me lazy if you want; I like to call it a sure thing. Sprinting with all my might, I arrive at the same time as my adversary. It's going to be a photo finish. I place my hand on the ball mere seconds before he does, ripping it out of his range before flicking it at him. It rebounds off his waist, and as he walks by me on the way to the prison, he mutters several expletives to describe his displeasure. I have no time to celebrate this success, however. I quickly move toward the back, so as not to be picked off early.

In the opening minute or two, things are relatively tranquil. Everyone has an innate fear of getting taken out, so the action is slow to start. A few cautionary armaments are thrown across each side, purposely aimed low to avoid being caught. They're tossed in an attempt to assess one another's guts and gusto, like two bears sizing each other up before going at it. The next few are thrown with a bit of topspin so as to go to the left or right of a perspective target; again, to avoid being caught, but this time with the intention of picking off a few players who are not giving the game the full attention that it constantly demands.

With a few kids in prison, the others rush forward to get them out. Our foes counter with an aggressive assault, and we take up a defensive position to try to take down the assailants. From this point on, pandemonium will be the dominant force surging through the minds of the masses. The biggest mistake that you can make in a game of prison ball is staring at someone or something. So much is coming at you at once that if you start focusing on just one part, chances are you won't last long.

Hanging out in the back, I tend to rely more on timing than on brute force. Strategy is key, but so is spontaneous instinct and nimble reflexes. Finding one of the larger yellow globules, I cast it at the legs of one of the taller contestants—their primary weak spots. After casting it toward him, I watch its arch as it dips too low and bounces harmlessly off the floor before reaching its destination. (I should mention, when they hit off the floors or walls, they discharge and can't get you out.) Josh tries to pull a fast one on me. Ever alert, I (in the best sense of the phrase) dodge the bullet. He gives me the kind of look that you would give to a cat that has just fallen down a flight of stairs—that of amazed, dumb-founded awe. I'm on to you now, Josh. I've got my eye on you. I'm watching you like a dyslexic hawk. The typical game activity continues for several minutes. Then, something happens.

Mike, as in the Mike kid from the bus, takes several steps toward dead center. In his hands he carries the two small red balls (yeah, real mature, guys)—the two deadliest torpedoes on the floor. We all simultaneously take several steps backward, stupefied by the calamity that is soon to befall us. One of these ravaging red orbs of bete noire are, in the hands of a skilled thrower, capable of being fired at well over fifty miles an hour. It's now an axiomatic game of chicken—he who blinks is the one who's going to get hit. And unless you're a really twisted masochist, getting pelted with one of these things is something to be avoided at all costs. Kate once got nailed in the head with one, and sustained a minor concussion. I think it was a miracle that she retained consciousness.

Mike takes great pleasure in seeing people cower before him. He can see that we're nervous. He can smell the sweat on our brows, the bile accumulating in our intestines. He launches the first one at maximum velocity. It screams past our eyes and hits someone in the arm, probably Joe. All you hear is a deaf scream of pure anguish off to the side somewhere. While I'm watching the sideshow, someone yells to me in a nervous panic, "Stefan! Look out! Look out! *Look out!*" It's Serena. The three notices are imperative. The first one lets me know that she wants my attention. The second one lets me know that something's wrong. The third one lets me know that the second ball is coming straight at me. Great.

I turn with just enough time to see Mike winding up for the pitch, his eyes locked with mine, a cruel smirk adorning his face. The next part is all mental. You've got to think matrix, and bend physics to their breaking point. Instinctively, I bow forward and drop to the floor, letting gravity and my body weight take me down as fast as possible. The next sound that I'll hear will either be the noise of the ball hissing past as it misses, or the resonance of impacted rubber as it collides with some part of my body. For a moment, everything seems calm and quiet. All other sonorities fall silent. It's the kind of stillness that most people associate with near-death experiences. I prefer to think of it as the eye of the storm.

hhhiiiiiiiiiiiiiiiiiiiiisssSSSSSSSssssssssssssss

You've got to love that sound. It lets you know just how close a call you had. This time I felt my hair ruffle in the breeze, or should I say the vortex, that it created. It's paradoxical almost, like being so close to Heaven and so close to Hell at the same time, existence and eradication being just inches apart. Today, I'm lucky—an unusual characteristic that rarely graces my presence. As I get up, I turn to Serena and kindly thank her for saving me from the ravages of a potentially major cranial impact.

Unfortunately, this is not always the case. Though I often consider myself talented in the art of prison ball—much in the same way Sun Tzu thought himself talented in the art of war—getting hit is almost inevitable. More often than not, I get called on some cheap shot. One of the slightly larger spheroids of destruction is thrown a little bit to the right of me. I try to catch it, but foolishly underestimate the fusillade celerity. I manage to touch the ball, only to watch it go straight through my hands with alarming rapidity. "*Shit!*" I mutter underneath my breath, as I walk to the chimerical crossbar hotel on the other side. On my way over, I look down and notice that my hand has been cut in several places. The raised rubber texture, which allows for a better grip, has sheared off several pieces of skin. I wrap my hand in my shirt to stem the bleeding.

Being in the pretend penitentiary is what gives prison ball its name (the prison part, anyway). If your people like you, and they're in a good mood, they'll free you as soon as they get a chance. You'll also have an edge over the others in with you if you're a decent athlete. If not, then prepare to rot in there for a while. Players springing someone from the clink put themselves at risk of getting hit, and unless everything is going pretty well for your side, you aren't worth the risk. This isn't to say that there's some kind of cult phobia against getting as many people out as possible. More often than not, getting someone out is seen as a noble act of bravery, and doing so whenever possible is the chivalric aspect of the game. A few, with perhaps more valor than brains, will even go down in an effort to liberate someone else. I know it seems that I've just contradicted myself in the same paragraph, but that's one of those great oddities of prison ball. Either that, or it's a testament to my random thought process.

From the looks of it, however, it would seem that I've picked the worse time to get knocked out. My fellow team members are dropping faster than the average American IQ, and the number of people capable of throwing a ball high and far enough to reach the lockup is growing smaller and smaller. One after another gets hit, and with each hit a small tear trickles down the countenance of hope. Then a voice, a docile and peaceable voice, shouts my name from across the gymnasium. "*Stefan!*" Well how do you like that? It's Serena! Normally she's one of the people who stands near the back and doesn't readily participate in athletic activities (she could care less about gym), but it would seem that she is rising to the challenge that our contingent of teenagers is facing. She wears an expression that is filled with the fire of determination, and thereupon gazing on it, my faith is restored. She lobs a ball with all the effort she has in her (which actually isn't that much, but beggars can't be choosers).

… It's coming in low, but it just might make it. Quietly whispering to myself, "Don't doubt, just take heart," I stare at it anxiously, praying with the kind of fervor that would put Buddhist monks to shame. Just maybe…just maybe…yes! I think it'll make it! As if in slow motion, it gradually descends toward my outstretched hands, as if guided by the hand of Fate. At that very instant, I swear I could hear a choir of angels singing praises to my good fortune. Kneeling on the floor, I manage to grab it just half a foot before it hits the ground. *Hallelujah!*

As I walk back to my side, I'll put my best efforts into putting on a nonchalant attitude, even though I possess no such thing. Serena gives me a smile. "Did you like that throw? It was *glorious!*" Indeed it was…indeed it was. With me now back in the echelon, as it were, my team rallies. I rescue the others at a speed that would lead you to believe that the gates of the prison have been broken and torn asunder. I have returned to free those who were held in bondage! Each shot volleyed from here on in strikes with deadly accuracy. Our opponent's flank breaks rank and flees under the barrage of fire, and on, and on, and on. The day is won—victory is ours! There you have it, really: the supernatural concept of life, death, and resurrection in such a seemingly basic activity. Who says kids shouldn't be playing this kind of stuff?

Prison ball, with all of its epic highs and lows, rigorous exertion, and far-fetched analogies to life in the broader scheme of things, is not the only activity of that magnitude that we partake of in our Personal Health and Fitness class. Nor is it the most malignant. No, the award for the most violent enterprise goes to pillow-polo.

Pillow-Polo:
Welcome to the Sanctum of Abaddon

Serious sport has nothing to do with fair play. It is bound up with hatred, jealousy, boastfulness, disregard in witnessing violence. In other words, it is war minus the shooting.
—*George Orwell*

Is there any good to be said about the game of pillow-polo? Maybe, maybe not. With people like Josh, Mike, Matt, Mikey, Joe, and myself, you don't really play it. You survive it. The game mechanics are simple enough: Each player is given a short stick, about three feet in length. At the end of that stick is a large, cylindrical-shaped piece of foam. This is where the "pillow" part of the name comes from. Using one of the small red balls (the kind you may recall me talking about in my section on prison ball), the players of each team try to hit the ball into the middle stack of bleachers on either side of the court, which serve as goals. The game is played on half the gym, with the dividers closed in order to provide a more intimate arena.

Aside from this, there are no official rules. There are no boundaries, and the only restriction is that the ball cannot be picked up with your hands (with the exception of the goalie, who enjoys this liberty). This is what would be called a "Sckonz Chaos Game." The ferocity of the frolic came when, early on, we discovered that we were not necessitated to be limited to only hitting *the ball* with our pillow-clad sticks. We, whether purposely or inadvertently, realized that a lot of the fun of the game could be derived from striking *each other*. From that point forward, Abaddon (in Hebrew mythology, the guardian of the pit and a personification of destruction) was our ally.

On a very rudimentary level, pillow-polo is a series of tests. It is a test of athletic ability, to see if we are on par with one another's vitality. It is a test of skill, as to who can pull off the coolest move, and who can whack the ball the hardest. And it is a test of endurance, as to who can sustain the most pain. It is important to mention that all of the previously mentioned people (excluding me) are, or were, very talented baseball players. They have the strength and capability to slam that ball around at whirlwind speeds. Likewise, they have the capability to slam that pillow-polo stick into *you*.

On a more sophisticated level, it is less of a game and more of a rite of passage than anything else—like an African hunt for lions that you must go on in order to be accepted by your village. If you pass, you shall forever be hailed as a hero and a man of character (or, at the very least, a psychopath). For once you show that you can strive, abide, and even thrive in the most daunting of tasks and situations, you have proven yourself to be someone who can compete on the ultimate level of play. And that, at the very least, says *something*. If you fail, you'll be dragging your sorry ass off the court in shame, not to mention that you'll be a target from now on. Might I regale you with a saga or two?

Fight or Flight?
Animal Instincts Take Center Stage

People who fight fire with fire usually end up with ashes.
—*Abigail Van Buren*

The lot of us—more often than not consisting of most of the guys in our coed, clad class—are divided into two teams. The color stick that is carried by the player, which come in two varieties (bluish green and amber yellow), distinguishes the two sides. Sckonz chucks the ball into the air, and the festivities begin. Right away, Mike, on the opposing team, goes after it. Pillow-polo is one of those unique games that brings out erratic qualities in people that they wouldn't normally show. Our animal instincts to kill or be killed replace our thinking and reasoning functions. I think this may be the best way to explain Mike's borderline demented demeanor. With the kind of tenacity that is most common in wild beasts and mythological creatures, such as the Minotaur of Crete or the multi-headed Hydra, Mike charges at the ball and pounds it. A blur of red zips across the court as several others go after it.

Another one of the unique aspects of pillow-polo is that only two or three people are actively engaged in it at any one time. The staggering pace at which the contest proceeds makes frantic running back and forth virtually pointless, so most of the people are at a standstill position until the ball comes into their general vicinity. The result is sudden bursts of barbarous behavior, and a nearly endless amount of potency to keep the game going. Mike is the exception to this generalization; he has a limitless supply of energy that allows him to do whatever he wants in this game.

By this time, Mikey, our goalie, has taken control of the ball. The standard way to hit the ball is to steady it first, either with the hands or with a vertical tap of the stick, and then take a full swing while it bounces. Mikey whacks it to the opposite corner, where it rattles around the space between the bleachers and the divider. Someone on our team, Seth, goes to try to take control of it. Hot on his heels is Mike, in full malign monkey mode. Whilst in the struggle to get the ball from Seth, he stops swatting at the ball and starts pummeling Seth himself. Each time he brings his bludgeon back, he follows with a downward thrust upon his hapless victim. He wallops with such fury that the stuffing from the pillow part of his staff is hacked to pieces, as fragments of debris surround him in a cloud-like manner. At last the ball is freed from the corner, and the beating is mercifully halted. For now.

As the ball springs to center court, I sprint to it and give it a one-arm swing. It ricochets off the top corner of the middle bleacher as the rest of my team rejoices, sharing in my triumph. I take a quick glance at Mike. He has impetuosity burning in his eyes. Shit, I've enraged the beast. Matt, the enemy goalie, has the ball. He drops it to the ground and prepares to swing. I, perchance rather foolishly, run forward to obstruct its flight with my body. As he's about to hit it, I turn my back on him and brace myself, half-longing to block it, half longing for it to miss me. A few moments later, I feel the severe impingement on my spine. Oh yes, that made contact. The ball recoils in another direction, but at this specific point of time, I don't have the energy or the ability to take off after it. At the moment, my mind is focused on the agonizing affliction radiating from the six-inch-square epicenter on my backside. It's a searing, burning pain, but hey, at least I blocked the ball, right?

By the time I regain my composure, the ball is at the other end of the room, where it would seem that Mike is about to score an easy goal on Mikey. Joe flings his stick at him, a common practice used in order to disrupt the flow of a player's motion and also to trip them. Mike, being the adept lunatic that he is, is able to quickly recover and prepares for a bone-shattering lash. On the back swing, however, a celestial being descends from above. Well, it's not a really a celestial being; it's just Josh (which means I should probably say it's a demonic being), but he *is* descending from above via his astounding vertical leap, and brings his cudgel down with him. Down it comes, clouting Mike's pillow-polo stick, cleaving it in two. The others shout in a hullabaloo, like rabid sharks going into frenzy over freshly spilt blood. Mike darts off to the storage closet to equip himself with a new prop—one that will be better suited to take on the abuse of our proceedings.

There's always a great rush of excitement that comes with being in the center of the action, but if you really want to get a feeling of what it's like to risk life and limb, I'd recommend that you try being the goalie. The position of goalie, unlike the kind in soccer, is not a quiet and laid-back position. It takes an immense amount of audacity, and absolute nerves of steel. These qualities are required, because you need to be cool under fire (literally) so that you'll have the fearlessness to obstruct the path of an object that's coming at you at hypersonic speeds.

It's not an easy thing, as I discovered during one game when I found myself standing in front of the middle bleacher, polo stick in hand, charged with guarding the mile-wide bull's-eye with my life. And the instant at which you're under the most pressure is when one of the opposing players is coming straight at you. They've got the ball in front of them, they're only a few yards away, and your defense is nowhere in sight. You're in the hot seat, because the precise moment at which someone has the most tempestuousness is right before they hit the ball in an effort to score a point. The adrenaline is pumping, the blood is boiling, and the testosterone has been shifted into overdrive. That thing is about to come at you at a speed that—to someone who has never seen it in action—can barely be perceived. Most rookies would freeze up at this critical moment, cover their head with their arms, and beseech Buddha for the best. But I'm not one of these types. I show some backbone, grunt, and tell the competition to bring it on!

So here comes Josh bounding toward me, seemingly intent on bringing it. He's about my height, give or take an inch. His odd shade of brown hair cut short and brought to a wave formation in the front with the aid of a great deal of gel (as is the style). His strength and vertical leap are both somewhat greater than my own, so I have every right to be uneasy. He's about ready to send that ball like a Hail Mary on heroine. He's looking for bragging rights, and there doesn't seem to be anything that anyone can do to stop him. I am not completely defenseless, however. I do have a trick up my sleeve. Mike has just recently stolen several other people's pillow-polo sticks, and given them to me. Instead of just one weapon, I now hold three. Josh is getting ready for the swing—I'll have to act now. All at once, that fire inside of me flares up. The sensation of bloodlust becomes so overpowering that I can practically taste it. And it is a sweet, sweet flavor.

Like so many specialist warriors before me, like a psychotic samurai, like an absurd Viking berserker, like a hysterical Hun horseman, I go on the warpath. I take each stick one at a time, and fling them in tomahawk fashion with all the strength I can focus into them. One after another they spin, each one nailing their intended target. First in the chest, then the left arm, and then the stomach. What now, bitch? *What now?!*

Killer kick-ass mode is what now, and Josh seems more than ready to embody it. He pauses for a moment, seemingly in shock at what I've just done. But the stunned sensation quickly passes, and he lets out a shout. Nay, a roar. A primitive roar, a diabolic roar—an inhuman roar. The message is clear: The maelstrom cometh. I can't say for sure, but I would have to maintain that this was the first time that I've ever felt that my Judgment was at hand. How would you feel if all of your nightmares were suddenly brought to life? All their horrors and hatreds suddenly manifested in the spirit of one person? I'll tell you one thing (and remember, I'm speaking from prior participation), you'd be scared shitless.

He reaches down and picks up one of the pillow-polo sticks, like Hephestus retrieving some sort of arcane weapon out of the forge of the gods, or Thor grabbing his infamous war hammer. Moving toward me at a full sprint, imbued with all the powers of perdition, he raises his club to the optimal smiting position. It is at this point that I realize that I've made one crucial mistake: I definitely, *definitely* should *not* have thrown *all* of my truncheons. All at once, he brings it down on me, intent on making his mark. Watching it come in, I calculate its path. It's somewhere around the fifty-, fifty-five-degree area. The point of balance will be right below the padding. Before he gets the chance to bash me to pieces, I catch his stave at the other end, and try to rip it out of his hands.

In his fit of rage, however, not even the strength of Arnold Schwarzenegger and Mahatma Gandhi *combined* would be able to pry the weapon from his vehement grip. He rips and twists his body in every direction, bent on removing the mace from my hand by any and all means. I won't let him have it that easy, though, and I remain steadfast in my conviction. The desperate tug-of-war lasted only ten to twenty seconds, but at the time it felt like we were battling for hours on end. It was like the Apocalypse was upon us, and I was combating the minions of Lucifer in a life-or-death endeavor to avoid total destruction. The outcome was uncertain, but for as long as I lived and breathed, I would not give in or give up to that tyrant of torment.

Alas, I knew in my heart that my efforts were in vain, as the incensed beast was not likely to let any force, human or not, halt his wrathfulness while it was in full motion. I finally let go in favor of running to the divider on the far side in order to arm myself with one of my previously used pieces of ammunition. As I made a mad dash to the other side, Josh showed that I'm not the only one with a proficiency in ax warfare. He slung his stick in some kind of sidewinder style. I was able to jump just in time to see it spin out across the floor below me. When I reached the ground, I furnished myself with two pillow-polo sticks, and turned to face my rival, who by then had outfitted himself with another stick of his own and the red bouncy ball. We approached each other, fully prepared to continue the battle to the death (or die trying).

He casts the ball at full force. It's moving too fast for me to see it coming, but a second later I feel a sharp pang at my hip on my left side. But this isn't going to deter me. Whatever efforts made now are futile. I seek an end to the means by which this was started, and I shall not rest until I have it. The time has come to stand and deliver! By the grace of Buddha, I go forth!

We bolt toward each other, and immediately engage once within range. This is the epic encounter of the age. Two great titans we are, locked in mortal combat. Each one predisposed to the other's annihilation. The engagement rages on in earnest. Swing and slice, slash and strike. Dodge, dodge, dodge, parry. Both of us are too equally matched to gain any headway, and soon become exhausted. We stare at each other from a short distance, each one waiting for the other to make the next move. Mike screams from the sidelines, "Hit him, Stefan! *Hit him!*"

Just when you think the madness is going to turn into mayhem, Sckonz comes in to tell us, in effect, to cease and desist. And with that, we all stop at once, and return our pillow-polo sticks to the storage room. On the way back to the locker room, we exchange stories about who got beat up the most. The biggest rule of etiquette in fierce games like this is that once the game is over, all hostilities between players must be terminated. The rituals that hold the high school societal fabric together dictate that animosity between players needs to stay on the court, and go no further. This is a case in point as to why rough gym classes do *not* cause more violence in real life. If anything, they act as a safety valve to release natural male aggressions at a slow, regular tempo, instead of letting them build up and spill over at inopportune moments. This idea may not work quite as well for someone whom the rest of the class just pelted for half an hour, who may come away with a sense of deep-seated desire for vengeance and become a manic depressive as a result. But hey! What are the odds of that happening, right? Right?...*God, I'm so alone ...*

The biggest part of pillow-polo games is the post-game status report. Or should I say damage report? I have several bruises on my back, a bit of a stinging feeling in my right leg, and a burning sensation across my forehead from where a ball skimmed it. On several occasions, I've had both hands bleeding profusely, from the back of my right and the thumb on my left, where it would seem that I was hit so hard that my skin split against the pressure of my own thumbnail. Mike has several cuts on the back of his right hand, as well as the humiliation of being pegged in the face. Josh has a deep red mark on his upper arm from our little battle earlier. For two weeks after, every time that he ran into me, he would roll-up his sleeve and point it out to me. "You see that?! *You* did that!" I guess he thought that some sympathy was in order.

"Hey Josh! How would you like a red badge of courage right up your ass?" I never actually said that, for that would be in bad taste. But I was thinking that, every time. Others have various other maladies in the legs, groin, and arms. There are only two things that we are penitent for: hitting someone in the face, and making someone else exude blood. Other than that, it's assumed to be a consequence of the game. As in due order, Mike profusely apologizes to me for the cuts on my hands; Josh to Mike for the face pegging.

Sckonz comes in after class and proclaims, "Mike! You should have been born in the sixties!"

Mike looks at him inquisitively, "Why, Sckonz?"

"Because you would've fit in nicely!" Several weeks later, prison ball and pillow-polo were forever banned from gym. During a game of prison ball, several girls (by which I mean bitches) decided that this uncivilized activity was somehow beneath them. So, in a passive protest, they resolved to sit on the bleachers located in back of where we were standing and not participate. When Sckonz gave the command to commence, Mike threw a standard-sized ball at top speed, purposely aiming low so as to hit someone in the torso or waist. The three or four kids standing in front of this particular girl saw the ball coming, and moved out of its path (as you might expect). However, since this girl was completely oblivious to its arrival, she didn't move accordingly. Furthermore, since this particular girl was sitting down, the ball nailed her precisely in the head. Her head proceeded to rebound off the bleachers, further promoting the injury. Once again, stupidity is what has caused the downfall, and passive resistance was not the golden solution that she likely speculated it was. The only difference is that now, the rest—from all of us to forever future generations—are going to have to suffer. Fuck state legislation—the passing of some of the greatest games ever created.

Incredi-Ball

With the absence of violent games like pillow-polo and prison ball, we had to proceed on to the next most-intense game we played, which was incredi-ball. The game of incredi-ball (pronounced like you would "incredible," except with an "a" sound after the "b") is played much in the same way that one would play baseball. Instead of baseball, the red super bouncy ball (the one that you may recall from the sections on prison ball and pillow-polo) is used. A standard metal bat is also utilized. It's played indoors with rules that are identical to baseball. Don't ask me where the name came from. Somehow, it just worked its way into our vocabulary. It quickly became just as tumultuous as anything else we played in gym. When everyone was trying to tag you out, you were really wishing that they missed when they whipped that thing at you at as fast as they could (much in the same way that they did in prison ball).

You would think that a game that so closely resembles baseball would be a joy to play, given all the baseball and softball players that we had in our class. And you would be entirely wrong. The weird thing about incredi-ball is that it takes perfectly reasonable, logical, skilled baseball and softball players, and turns them into completely illogical assholes. Much like what politics does to certain people, you might say. I'm not the most knowledgeable person when it comes to baseball, but I do know

that if there's a person on first and there's a person on third, trying to get the person on third out is a higher priority than getting
the person on first out. They, too, probably knew this. But if they
did, they sure as hell didn't act like they did. The kind of twist
that gym puts on sports makes you wonder what's really happening to our thought process. On any given game, I can get more
applause from getting hit with the ball and taking my base than I
could from hitting a home run. That's a fact.

Besides this, the bouncy ball has such an incredible amount of
elasticity that you only get one throw at someone. If you miss, the
ball is going to bounce around the gym for an intolerably long
time, and when you finally do get hold of it, the person you originally threw it at has had ample time to make it home, or at least
to the next base or two. In incredi-ball, you either win or lose by
a lot. There aren't a lot of close games. Sure, you might feel good
about yourself when the score is 27–3 in your favor, but at that
point you start to wonder, "Why bother?"

Nowhere was this better illustrated than in one particular
play that Joe had made. Now, Joe was a hairy, muscular, gorilla-
shaped, five-foot-five kid who was aptly adept in baseball. He
was, however, for whatever reasons, incomprehensibly cursed at
incredi-ball. During one game, with the bases loaded (or "juiced,"
as Sckonz would call it), the ball was hit with a bit of a spin that
sent it onto the stage (which is fair play). Joe jumps up on there,
gets it, and prepares to chuck it at someone running from second
to third. He throws like he would a baseball during game
time...and misses completely. I mean, he wasn't even close. He
wasn't even close to "close." If I may use a baseball analogy at this
point, he wasn't even in the ballpark. He wasn't so much as in the
parking lot of the ballpark. He was in F-lot somewhere.

The ball is also going way too fast for any one of us in the
infield, midfield, or outfield to catch it, either. So Joe runs after it.
He jumps off the stage, runs into the middle of the gym, and
grabs it after it's been rebounding off the walls in the back for
what seems like forever. Joe has one more chance to redeem himself. If he can nail the last runner who's going home, we might be
able to forgive him. He throws it again...and misses completely.
Again. With that, he stands in the middle of the gym for several
minutes, thinking about how bad you have to be in order to make

two errors in the same play, let alone the same inning. Only one of the other kids in the class, Eric by name, has the voice to break his trance-like state. He offers Joe this piece of advice: "Nice goin,' you dumb fuck!" and nails Joe squarely in the face with the same ball that he could not make any use of.

When Mikey is pitching, it's always a show. He once bounced the ball off the backboard of the basketball hoop, then off his arm, then dribbled off his legs several times before letting it fall into a drop kick for the pitch. The ball screamed past the batter's head as he enthusiastically shouted, "Strike one!" It all wasn't really that bad.

The G.A. Gig

Once I had finished gym for the quarter (it is a semester your freshman year, a half of a semester during your sophomore), I had no intention of staying put in some boring study hall. I needed action! I needed excitement! What I got, and quite unexpectedly, was a period where I got to be the "Gym Assistant," a type of independent study for other physical education classes. For those of you not familiar with the inner-workings of our school system bureaucracy, the whole process of becoming one of the fabled elite (and I use the term loosely) of the gym assistants is, at best, a shady deal. There are a lot of favors played, and there are a lot of plea bargains made. This is all amplified by the fact that there are absolutely no requirements in order to be admitted. I pulled some strings, and a few days later, both Kate and I landed spots during a period that was hotly being sought after by a multitude of others. A testament to my control over the system? Perhaps, but power is, at best, an illusion. Just ask Mussolini.

Kate and I are standing there at the orientation speech that Sckonz gives to all of his classes on the first day. His advice rarely changes much: "Just keep it cool, play it safe. I know some of you kids at your age—you're getting your first kiss, drinking your first Miller, and listening to your first Zeppelin album, and you're just going nuts! Let's try to keep it under control. We've already lost a few sports this year ..." As he adds that last part, Mike casts his head down and turns away. He then turns to us for the formality of introductions. "And we've got Katelyn, and we've got Koski helping us out! Let's give 'em a hand!" Some of them clapped, some of them gave us "the look." I make a quick mental note of who isn't applauding, so that I can make a list later.

Sckonz was always like that. Although not particularly tall, he was, in the best meaning of the term, jacked. His shaved head gleaming in the light and a warmhearted smile painted across his face, he was absurdly optimistic, round-the-clock. You could walk outside with him on any given day, and he would spit out a piece of phraseology like, "Wow! What a beautiful day! The sun is shinin,' the birds are singin'...It's a great day to be alive, and it's an even better day to be a gym teacher! Wouldn't you say so, Kosk?" He always uses the last names of his students when addressing them. With all the "Mikes" in this school, I don't blame him.

"Mr. Sckonz, I was under the impression that every day was a great day to be a gym teacher."

With this, his face lights up and he instinctively extends his hand to shake mine. "Good answer, Kosk! Yes, that is the correct answer! Check-plus in the book. *Alright!* " That was the standard word that he used at the close of every thought. It was his way of boldfacing his speech. He shakes my hand with an iron grip. A "Nixon handshake" is what he calls it. I'm guessing that he's implying pre-Watergate Nixon.

First order of business is to clean up the storage closet in the gymnasium. Let me impart a little piece of knowledge to you: Numerous teachers and heads of authority have given this command to numerous subordinates. It's simply not going to happen. That thing has been a mess for years, and it will continue to be a mess for as long as it exists, or at the very least for as long as it's in use. Having been given this order many times before, I naturally have plenty of experience as to how to handle it. I go in there and push everything to the side that I'm able to push to the side. This normally includes basketballs, nets, and cardboard boxes of every size imaginable. Then, I take whatever I can physically lift, and hoist it onto the uppermost shelves. Regions where no one, and I mean absolutely no one, will find them for years to come.

To get a mental image of what that's like, just picture the warehouse from *Indiana Jones and the Raiders of the Lost Ark*. After about five minutes or so, everything looks better. It's certainly not any cleaner, but aesthetic appeal is like Japanese yen—worth nothing, buys everything...I'm pretty sure that's how Japanese yen works.

The next task is to clean up yet another closet filled with worthless junk. This time it is the old health education material, mostly consisting of old books, pamphlets, and videos. We haven't had a real health class in our high school in quite some time, and the educational matter makes this glaringly obvious— "Cocaine: The Perfect Way to Start Your Day!" A whole bunch of them were telling me to think twice before smoking something called "Mary Jane." From the looks of it, it would seem that it's bad for you.

Everything screamed flashback, which is not a good thing. Like that movie, *Dazed and Confused*—the entire thing was reminiscent of a flashback. And it was a shitty flashback. If you think this film was a culture-bending and -blending cult comedy classic, you deserve to be dragged out into the street and shot. But you have to be dragged, or else it doesn't have the same effect. You have to be shot because there is no way we're risking the chance that you might pass on your genes to yet another generation of dumbasses.

I watched this movie on a weekday afternoon because Comedy Central doesn't have much in the way of an afternoon lineup, so they use shit like this as a backup. And it was shit, because there was no plot. Anyone, and I mean *anyone*, who went to *any* kind of film school of *any* reputable quality would know that the first step in creating a movie is to create a plot. That's the very first thing that they teach you. I hate flashbacks.

Most of this antiquated health education crap had to be disposed of at the proper waste receptacle, a.k.a. the dumpster. Who had the unenviable job of trekking out to the dumpster? Kate was the first to proclaim, "That's all you, Stefan!" Sure, why not? What could possibly be so bad about something as simple as that? I head outside, and the first thing that I notice is that it's raining, snowing, and sleeting, *at the same time*. Great. One of the only times that I'm outside during school hours, and I'm stuck with weather conditions that defy the laws of nature.

Every now and then, Sckonz will let you join in on one of the sports. "Who's winning? Shirts? Well, I guess I'll have to put Koski in for yellow!" Thank you, Mr. Sckonz. Being placed on the losing team midway through the game has always been my dream. They're all playing soccer, so I'm not what you would call "thrilled." I don't bring the crazy like I do for other games (like the kind that were banned). But there are no worries this time around. Even though psycho Mike is playing (why he's in yet another gym class is beyond me), after a quarter of putting up with all kinds of anguish, I've become somewhat impervious to pain.

Mike is goalie, and he's got the ball. I go up to block it with (what else?) my body. You can tell right away by the twinkle in his eye that he's about to launch this thing at me faster than a torpedo from the Red October. He drops the ball for the kick, and I turn my back to him and brace for impact. SMACK! It hits me dead center. Had he done this at the beginning of our gym class three months ago, I'd be howling in agony. But now, I barely feel a thing. I turn around, look at him, and just shrug my shoulders.

Someone else whom I tried to block had the wonderful idea that he was going take me down a notch. He kicked that ball about ten times harder than what was necessary. The joke was on him, though, because it bounced off my lower abdomen and into the goal. Purely coincidental to be sure, but I still got props for it. Yes, that's right—I used the word "props," a term from the ghetto lexicon. Now *there's* something that should be taught as a second language.

The Pleasantly Enjoyable Experience

The days that make us happy make us wise.
—*John Masefield*

What most of us get out of the physical education exploit is a class in which we genuinely enjoy ourselves. To take a break from the regular thing of sitting in one study group or another, listening to trivial information of one sort or another, and allow ourselves to feel like the day actually had some meaning to it. All the drama, hardships, and difficulties that bother us in day-to-day life can be forgotten, at least for a short while, so that we can partake in something that will give us gratification and peace of mind. Of all the supposedly important classes that we'll be forced to take over the course of our academic careers, how many can boast that they offer that kind of comfort? Even if I was to take on an optimistic point of view for once (perish the thought), I would have to say very few.

After we finish changing, we head back out into the gym to await the next bell. The air is filled with the sounds of our own sets of dialogue and lively conversations. You could say that everyone is gossiping, but this would be most inappropriate considering that guys don't gossip. Guys might have discussions about daily occurrences, but we don't gossip. Much in the same way that guys don't shop. We might go into stores and buy stuff, but we don't shop. But I digress, as I am too tired to go on disputing such differences.

As I stand here, staring into space, quietly laughing to myself as I imagine what would happen if one of the basketball hoops were to suddenly burst into flames, the bell rings. It's time to journey on, to leave this comfort zone, this safe haven that we've created for ourselves. We are so close to lunch, and yet so far away. We still have to endure one more class. And that class is English.

Miscellaneous Philosophy — Part 4
You Can Tell That It Was Written on a Friday

I originally got the idea for a novel while watching television. There was a commercial on that was funded by the United States Navy in which the low-toned announcer asked, *"If someone wrote a book about your life, would anyone want to read it?"* Ironically, instead of inspiring me to join the navy, it provoked me to write a book.

Say This Five Times Fast:
There were several ska sasquatches shaped like saxophones playing hopscotch with squash in Saskatchewan.

Have you ever been on a computer that has told you, "Push Any Key To Continue," and you had to stop and think about which key you wanted to push? Yeah, it probably is just me.

On a box of LUCKY CHARMS: Servings Per Container, About 13.

Have you ever seen these commercials that portray the perfect family? And they're always gathering for breakfast? That's not realistic. You see these ideal families: parents—not divorced; food—on the table; crack—safely hidden away.

My definition of "Cult-Classic": A film or television show that nobody has ever heard of, that gained no commercial recognition, that nobody cares about, that has to be seen/bought/recognized because somehow society is conspiring against it in order to keep it from reaching the public—all of whom would, theoretically, absolutely love it should they ever find out about it (which they won't).

I hate when people write e-mails that have the phrase "I'll talk to you later," because they never do. They just write more e-mails.

The great philosophical maxim of the age:
If a kangaroo has a computer, he probably stole it.

Chapter Seven

It's nearly impossible to get lost on the way to English class. You head out the door from the gym and go south, straight down the hall. You can smell the latest concoctions from the foods rooms. No matter what they're making or baking, it always smells better than the scents drifting from the cafeteria. No astonishment here. This is the only class that I have down this hallway, where the entrances to the library and the computer rooms are located, among other things. It's the oldest part of the building, solid brick, students pouring out of the "DOWN" stairs a little ways off. Getting here is like swimming upstream a firehose. Hall traffic is mostly touch and go, and at any second you could collide into one of the oncoming individuals who are parading toward you in endless procession. Thank Buddha that the doors open inward and not outward.

It's the fifth door on the right. Right away, you have to be careful. The little sign on the door says "PULL," but don't believe it for a second. Enough of us have lost it as it is. You have to trust me on this one: Push the door inward. See? That's what we would call a trust exercise. If you want some more of that, face away from a friend and tell them to catch you as you fall. But be absolutely certain that they are one of your better friends. (As you might have guessed, I don't trust a lot of people anymore.) While you're walking in, you'll notice that there's a little sign on the inside of the door that says, "PUSH." Well, this was the sociology room at one point, so perhaps this is just some twisted test in psychology. Either that, or one of the janitors has been hitting the bottle again.

The room itself is rather spacious compared to other rooms. The ceiling is about ten feet higher than in any other classroom, which gives it an unusual, Sistine Chapel feel. Our teacher has offered to decorate it with whatever is to our liking in an effort to

91

reduce its vastness, but my idea of writing "GIVE UP" in large lettering across the wall was quickly shot down. Something about sending the wrong message during parent-teacher conferences.

I take my seat in the middle row, third from the front. I walk down my chosen, alphabetically ordered row, with Josh in the first seat on the left and Serena on the first seat on the right. The modern Pillars of Hercules they are, sitting with relaxed and unconcerned faces, slouched in their chairs. Upon arriving at my seat, I see John. He's a tall man by all justifications, hair jet black, nicknamed "Mohegan" on the account of his dark brown skin. If there ever was a person who cared the least about English in this class, it's John. His talk of distaste for English is the only thing I can understand, as the rest of it is permanently scrambled with gear-head jargon, something that I've never been able to fully comprehend. Vocabulary assignments are always an adventure, with him asking me, "Hey Stefan! What comes first: 'R' or 'S'?"

"'R,' John. It hasn't changed since the last time you asked me." You can't blame him for it. Gear-head jargon tends to cripple one's other language skills. From time to time, he'll give me a warn-ing—"Head's up!"—shortly before he slams his desk into mine, which then slams my desk into the desk in front of me. It's John's form of communication. I eagerly await the day that he starts writing notes. But knowing John, that day is not likely to arrive any time soon.

In all honesty, English is definitely one of my personal favorites. It's one of the few classes in which I can really be myself without threat or fear of retribution (which is what I get from just about every other place in the world). This is mostly thanks to my English teacher, whom I was fortunate to have during both my freshman and sophomore years.

Mr. Denis was his name, and he was a man of character. He was a former mayor of our town who turned to teaching English at the town's high school. To this day, I haven't quite been able to figure out why someone would make either career choice. Nonetheless, there was a lot to like about his teaching style, which could best be described as two parts unconventional, and one part performance. I bring it up because it was, in my honest opinion, the only class that encouraged my creative stylings. We were often offered the chance to turn stories into skits, read in front of the class, and given the opportunity to use creative writing. This last part was the biggest perk, especially considering that our public school system has been locked in a do-or-die struggle to pound persuasive writing into our heads for the last four years (fifth grade through eighth). That's among my list of supporting facts of how high school made me dumber, and came frighteningly close to crushing my innovative thought process for good.

The great irony of the whole school system is that in their efforts to build us up in preparation for the real world, they almost completely broke us down. When I finished seventh grade, I would estimate that my IQ was about 135 (relatively intelligent). On an IQ test that I had taken a few months before the end of my freshman year, it had come down to 108 (average). Slacking in other subjects was the only way to help assert some kind of damage control. It makes me a little nervous, because I still have a couple more years to go, and anything below 80 is considered mentally retarded.

Maybe this is the place where I found out that I had a desire to entertain. It was the ultimate forum where I could express both my dramatic and comedic insight, and was the greatest, cheapest self-esteem booster I could ever ask for. Just about any adolescent will tell you that the approval of their peers is the greatest triumph that can ever be ascertained, and this was one of the few places that I found it.

The standard day-in, day-out tasks are, in a word, standard. We'll read several short stories or poems aloud, then answer a few questions. Simple things, really. I always enjoyed being the one who started reading a poem or story out loud; to be the one who could speak the title and author with the utmost articulation, like the announcer for PBS who tells you, "This program is brought to you by the Corporation for Public Broadcasting, and by annual financial support from viewers like you." Some might say that I'm desperate for attention, but I've never thought of myself as desperate. Or crazy. Never crazy. Do you think it's weird that I brought that up without reason?

So Mr. Denis gets up in front of the class with the big-ass teacher's edition of the *Elements of Literature* book. He sits on the edge of his desk, his feet sheathed in well-polished dress shoes, balanced on a sideways-standing chair in front of him. He's of average height, with black hair—interlaced with gray patches— that swirls in an almost kind of roll that creeps farther and farther in front of his head with each passing day until he bothers to get it trimmed back. His moustache is the same way, except it doesn't really "swirl" as much. He starts every class with a "Good morning" (or "Good afternoon," when appropriate), and won't go any further until he gets a response from everyone. He was very good at this whole "teaching" thing, as marked by the way he handled his students. He knew that the best way to win was to fight fire with fire, or in this case, apathy with apathy. Whenever he gave an assignment, and someone would say, "I don't care about this, Mr. Denis," his reply was, "I don't care if you don't care! Get to work!" Why didn't anyone think of that sooner?

Before he starts any kind of teaching, he'll amuse us with a story. I'm not sure where he got it from, but the man has an impeccable ability for telling anecdotes of his day-to-day life, which makes it seem like anything but day-to-day. Even if you don't like the yarn, you'll still enjoy the amount of time that it kills. As is appropriate, I'll include a few little samples of them. Remember, I'm not being untruthful about any of this; these are all direct quotes:

"So I had the movers coming up one morning to deliver a bunch of furniture...and they don't speak *any* English..." (This was followed by a lengthy, detailed discussion of how he conned the Hispanic movers into getting rid of the cardboard boxes that the furniture came in.)

"While I'm in the lobby, I start making a scene, saying things like, 'I'm glad to see you got rid of all the caution tape!' And he's (the manager) looking at me with a look of horror and telling me, 'Dave! Be quiet!' and I'm going off, 'Well, I'm just saying that you got all the blood out of the carpet and it just looks great!'...So in the end, I got the room for free.

"But I tell you, my wife is trying to kill me. She won't be happy until the house is completely destroyed. The house insurance is the first bill that I pay each month ...

"During college was when I started pulling all-nighters...My brother and I were studying for finals one night at three in the morning, and my father, who was working two shifts and occasionally came down during the night, saw us at the table and looked at the clock that said 'three'…He's not really awake when he first wakes up, so he's not really sure what's going on. He asks us, 'What time is it?'

"I said, 'Dad, it's three.'

"And he's thinking that it's three in the afternoon, so he says, 'Why didn't anyone wake me up?'

"I said, 'Well, we just got home, we just opened our books…'

"He says, 'I'm going to be late for work!'

"I told him, 'Well, you'd better get going! I'll make you lunch.'

"Now my younger brother was going to tell him the whole thing right then and there, but I told him, 'Don't you say a word!' He just sat there with his face buried in his hands. Now my father is up in the bathroom getting ready, and we can hear the water running and everything…It hadn't occurred to him to look out the window. He comes down all ready for work, and he looks outside the window to see what kind of a day it is, and he can see that it's pitch black. So now he's really confused. He turns to us, and then he turns to the clock, and asks us, 'What time is it?'

"I said, 'Dad, it's three in the morning, what are you doing up?'

"'Didn't I just come down here…and you said you were going to make me lunch?'

"No, you didn't. This is the first that we've seen of you.

"'Was I dreaming?'

"You must've been…you should go back upstairs and get some sleep.

"He goes back upstairs and my mother is asking him, 'Were you just in the shower?'

"'I don't know. I must be going crazy.'

"I'm going casting later today. Some call it 'fishing.' I call it 'casting' because 'fishing' implies that you're catching fish."

"I have a cat with only one eye named 'Herby'…It's fun on Halloween because I dress him in an eye-patch like a pirate. Of course, I put the eye-patch over the *good* eye, so…"

"I was the one who, when I was a kid, I wouldn't go into the sandbox because then I would get my clothes all dirty. My mother would say, 'Dave, don't you want to go and play in the sandbox?' And I'd take one look at it and say, 'Nope.'"

I probably should have also mentioned that he's hopelessly germaphobic. Which makes everything that much more farcical. A few weeks before Christmas, he was telling us, "For those of you buying me gifts, I'd like you to keep a twenty-dollar spending limit." With this, his hand slips and knocks his empty coffee mug to the floor. "You can get me a new coffee mug...I obviously can't use this one anymore."

So after he's done with story time, if you could call it that (and some do), he'll start with the lesson for the day. "Open your books to page 507 and we'll start on..." He starts inadvertently staring out into the hallway. "Is that Debb?" Well, he sure is picking an odd time to make small talk with the office secretary. "Debb! *Debb*! Can you get my coffee?!"

A voice from the hallway replies, "Where is it?"

"It's in the microwave!"

"No, it's not! It's sitting next to it!"

"You mean someone touched it? Well, I can't drink it now!"

Romeo, oh Romeo...Where the Hell Are You?

English in high school is when you really get a chance to familiarize yourself with the classics, even if you have no desire to do so. Now and then you'll hear critics (assuming you actually listen to critics) say, "There aren't any more classical authors like Shakespeare and Sophocles." There's just one key problem with this generalization—neither of these guys were very proficient in their profession.

Right now, after reading that last statement, I can tell that you're probably thinking two things. The first is, "Isn't that typical of a teenager to poke fun of such prominent figures in history?" And the second is, "Who the hell is Sophocles?" The second one is easy: Sophocles was one of the first in a line of leading philosophers in ancient Greece. His protégé was Plato, and his protégé was Aristotle. The first question, however, requires some explaining.

Let's start with Shakespeare. To the lot of us, I'm sure it's exceedingly difficult to understand whatever it is that he's talking about. This aside, most of his plays are pretty well written. They're filled with plot twists, tension, intrigue, and foreshadowing. In other words, all the qualities of a good story, with the exception of the ending. Old Will never seemed to be quite capable of writing a good finale, so instead he overcompensated with lots of death to create one. In *Romeo and Juliet*, I'm sure most of us are aware that both Romeo and Juliet die (and if you weren't, I apologize for ruining the ending). In addition to these two tortured lovers, several other people are also liquidated. If my memory serves, first someone in Juliet's family kills someone in Romeo's family. Then Romeo kills someone in Juliet's family. Then another unrelated character kills one of Romeo's friends. On his way to find Juliet, Romeo duels and kills several other people. I don't know how many of you have actually read *Romeo and Juliet*, but by the story's conclusion, there are twenty-something people who have been slain. Was it all really necessary?

Then there is the always-popular play, *The Tragedy of Julius Caesar*. After the initial suspense is lost—as we already know what's going to happen to Caesar as soon as we read the title—the rest of it kind of goes downhill from there. After Caesar is murdered, Brutus, Cassius, and Brutus's wife, Portia, kill themselves. I just don't get this unhealthy obsession with using death and suicide to spice up a story.

Sophocles also made this overkill (yes, pun intended) wrap-up mistake. The best (and not coincidentally, the only) example that comes to mind is that of *Antigone*, a play about obeying the laws of the State versus obeying the laws of the gods—something that obviously troubled the Greeks on a regular basis. (Important note: I'm referring to the second part of *Antigone*, as it is a long epic divided into several parts.) So as the story goes, this guy Eteocles is ruling the city of Thebes (the one in Greece, not Egypt), and is supposed to be taking turns ruling it with his brother, Polynecies. But being the selfish little bastard that he is, Eteocles refuses to give his brother a turn. Not only does Polynecies go off to Argos (another city in Greece) to bitch about it, he also raises an army there and uses it to attack Thebes. Although his army loses, both Eteocles and Polynecies manage to kill themselves, as was the style of the time.

The king of Thebes, Creon, orders Eteocles to be given a hero's funeral, since he was, in a word, a hero. But he also decrees that Polynecies should not be given a burial, and consequently be left to rot. This angered the Greeks, and Creon's niece, Antigone, who believed that in order for the soul of someone to be at peace and not lie in torment in Hades, a proper burial must be given. Hence the conflict between Creon and Antigone, between the laws of the State and the laws of the gods. What the hell am I supposed to do with all that information now?

I'm fairly familiar with it since it was one of the plays that we read aloud in class, something that was Mr. Denis's hallmark. I read the part of King Creon. I also sang the part of the Chorus. No, that is not a typo—I was the *entire* Chorus. All fifteen members of it (who were, hypothetically, supposed to be fifteen elders of Thebes). I was the only one with the guts (nay, the talent) to sing in front of the rest of the class. And if I were to stroke my ego, which I do on occasion, I would have to say that I did a bang-up job…Wow, that's a bad word to use—"bang-up."

We could discuss the incest issue that arises from Creon's son, Haimon, being engaged to Creon's niece, Antigone, but we won't. Or at least, I won't. You're more than welcome to enjoy your sick fantasies. Skipping to the ending, though, Antigone kills herself. You might have seen that one coming. Then Haimon kills himself. Okay, that's a bit of a stretch, but I'll buy it. Then Creon's wife, Eurydice, kills herself. Alright, now this whack-job thinker has gone too far. Imagine if we were to come up with bumper stickers for *Antigone*—

Suicide: Make the Commitment

WWZD—What Would Zeus Do?

My Other Car Is A TROJAN HORSE!

I'm not quite sure if I got that last one. Wouldn't it be weird if someone wrote a script to Creon's court trial after all this happened? Well, it's funny that you should bring that up, because it just so happens that I did! And here it is:

(Note: The part of the judge was played by none other than Mr. Denis himself; King Creon was played by Mikey; the defense was played by Serena; and the prosecution was played by me at the time of our performance. As an additional side note, Teiresias was the blind prophet who warned Creon of his impending doom. You'll understand when you see it.)

ANTIGONE
TRIAL AND TRAVAIL
BY STEFAN KOSKI

JUDGE: Trial case number seven, zero, four, seven, six, three—the People versus King Creon of Thebes. On the three accounts of manslaughter, two accounts of murder in the second degree, and grave indifference to human life, how do you plead?

CREON (Mikey): Not guilty, your honor.

JUDGE: Defense, your first witness?

DEFENSE (Serena): Your honor, I'd like to call my first and only witness to the stand, King Creon of Thebes. (*Audience gasps. Mikey gets out of his seat and approaches the witness stand.*)

JUDGE: Raise your right hand. (*Mikey does so.*) Do you swear to tell the truth, the whole truth, and nothing but the truth, so help you Zeus?

C: I do.

D: King Creon, can you describe, to the best of your ability, what happened on the day of the deaths of your son, niece, and wife?

C: (Distraught) Well…I had just woken up around two o'clock in the afternoon. I had had a little wine the night before, and felt like sleeping in later than usual. I walked into the palace throne room, when Teiresias comes in…He told me that I should reconsider my decision to kill Antigone.

D: And what was your response?

C: I told him to shove it, that I didn't need an advice from some blind bum of a prophet.

D: How did the counsel feel about this decision?

PROSECUTION (Stefan): Objection! Leading!

JUDGE: Sustained.

D: How did the counsel react to this decision?

P: Objection, leading.

JUDGE: Overruled. Answer the question, King Creon.

C: Choragos came up to me, and told me to stop acting like an idiot and fix things.

D: And you took this advice to heart?

C: Yes...I finally saw the errors of my ways...but...*(starts sobbing)* it was too late...It was all too late! Now I've lost everything! *(Sobs inconsolably.)*

D: *(In comforting tone)* It's okay, good King, it's okay. *(To the judge:)* No further questions, your honor.

JUDGE: Prosecution, your witness.

P: *(Clears his voice and pauses to gather his thoughts.)* King Creon. King ta-ding ta-ding ta-ding, ding-ding-ding-ding Creon. The big Crenola. The Crenster. The Crenomeister. King Creon.

C: *(Unsure)* Yes? ...

P: Where were you on Thursday morning of last week?

C: I was, uh... in the palace.

P: *(Making a big deal out of the answer)* In the palace, you say? I see...What exactly was it that you were doing in the palace?

C: *(Contemplating and carefully choosing his words)*...Probably doing the usual King law-administering thang, I don't know...I don't really remember.

P: You don't remember?! Were you enjoying some of the royal hash or were you just celebrating a Dionysus festival?

D: Objection! Battering the witness!

Judge: Sustained. Counsel, try to keep your remarks within reason.

C: *(Offended)* No, it was just the same old thing, y'know—rule the city, enforce the laws, etcetera, etcetera.

P: Is that so? Do you remember what you were doing on Wednesday of last week?

C: *(Suspicious)*...Yes.

P: *(Excitedly exaggerated)* Well, don't just leave us in the dark, King Creon, if that is your real name. Tell the jury what you were doing!

C: *(Reluctantly)* I was giving Antigone her sentencing.

P: *(Sarcastically surprised)* You were sentencing your own niece to death?!

C: Yes...I was.

P: Was there anyone who spoke out against this decision?

C: Yes...Teiresias and Choragos.

P: AND?!

C: *(Sorrowfully)* My son, Haimon.

P: Was not your son, Haimon, engaged to your niece, Antigone?

C: *(Pestered and rolling his eyes)* Yes.

P: King Creon, is it true that you are your own father's sister's friend's neighbor's cousin's girlfriend's uncle's son-in-law?

C: NO!

P: Are you sure?

C: *(Pausing to think it over)*...Yesss ...

P: So you willingly sentenced your niece to death?

C: Yes ...

P: Did you not think that the stress and turmoil of losing his fiancée could cause the death of your son?

C: No!

P: Didn't he tell you that the death of Antigone would cause the death of another?

C: Well, yes, but he meant my death!

P: Did he? Did he, King Creon?

C: Yes! He tried to kill me!

P: *(Overdramatizing)* Oh! Oh dearest me! Haimon has tried to kill the "good" King Creon! Perhaps we should put him on trial! Oh, that's right, *(exaggerates the point)* he's dead! How convenient.

D: *(Annoyed)* Objection, your honor!

JUDGE: On what grounds?

D: Any grounds!

JUDGE: *(After briefly considering)* I'm going to allow this.

P: And what about your wife, Eurydice?

C: *(Frustrated)* Yes, she's dead too.

P: Didn't you think that the death of your niece and son would cause her great distress?

C: I had no control over how she felt or what she did.

P: No control?! She was a woman, was she not? Does not a man have control over his own household and his own wife?!

D: Objection!

JUDGE: Overruled.

C: Yes, she was a woman! But I had no idea ...

P: *(Heating up his argument)* You had no idea?! Did you also have no idea of what was happening in your own State? In your own government?! My God, man! Did you have any idea what you were doing at all?!

C: *(Losing control of himself)* No! I mean, yes! It was all just happening so fast! First she was dead, and then...and then he was dead...and then...I didn't know what to do next.

P: You killed your niece!

C: NO!

P: You killed your son, too, didn't you?!

C: NO! That's not true!

P: You killed your wife! You killed all three of them!

C: *(Sobbing and yelling at the same time)* NO! THAT'S NOT TRUE!

P: You're a cold and heartless king who had no idea what he was doing!

C: NO! NO, I NEVER—

P: You killed your family—what's next? The city?! The State?!

C: No, I just...I just wanted...*(voice trails off)*

P: *(Short pause)* King Creon, isn't true that you're a racist?

D: OBJECTION!

P: *(Quickly)* Withdrawn. No further questions your honor. *(Takes his seat.)*

JUDGE: You may step down, King Creon. *(Mikey does so.)* Defense?

D: The defense rests, your honor.

JUDGE: Prosecution?

P: The prosecution rests, your honor.

JUDGE: Counselors, your closing arguments?

D: *(Gets up slowly to address the jury [audience]. She makes her speech soft and heartfelt.)* Ladies and gentlemen of the jury, King Creon was a good king, with good intentions. He wanted the best for his family and for the State. He is only human—he makes mistakes, just like you and I. Do not judge him on his past mistakes; judge him on his character. His good, kind-hearted character. *(Takes her seat.)*

P: *(Gets up and paces several times back and forth in order to pick the right words. He makes his speech hard and to the point.)* Good people of the jury, look at the man sitting right there *(points to Mike)*. Do you see that man? Do ya? That man sentenced his own niece to death. *(Pauses for emphasis.)* That man killed his niece, his son, and his wife! The good King Creon is nothing more than a cold-hearted murderer. He murdered his family, he murdered the State, and now he wants to murder the justice system. I, too, want you to judge him on his character. The character of a killer—of a man who has no regard for human life OR human suffering. I ask you, I implore you; do not judge wrongly, as this man has. *(Takes his seat.)*

THE END?

The whole thing was a smash hit with my English class, which applauded for upward of fifteen seconds! It was so good, in fact, that all three of us earned a "A" for the project, and I was asked to make an appearance in two other class skits of the same assignment. I played a drunken guard who was an eyewitness (and to whom I gave a voice that bore a striking resemblance to that of Boomhower from *King of the Hill*) and Zeus (just imagine Bing Crosby after chugging a Red Bull).

Overall, we had a lot of fun in English class. I certainly don't have a lot of bad memories of it—with the exception of one. And that one exception is:

CAPT (Crappy Ass Preparation Test) Practice

They say hard work never hurt anybody, but I figure, why take the chance?

—*Ronald Reagan*

Who could ever forget the CAPT practice? In all honesty, it stands for the Connecticut Aptitude Performance Test, and it is the infamous exam (mentioned briefly in Chapter 6) that all students, starting with my class, have to pass in order to get out of high school. During the CAPT, whoever is proctoring the test has to read a boat-load of bullshit about all sorts of things like using No. 2 pencils, and "Today you'll be taking the blah blah blah..." Included in the mantra of each section is the statement, "There is nothing special that you have to do in order to prepare for this test." Ah, but there is! You have to take all sorts of meaningless CAPT practice dittos! *Liars*! What if no one wanted to take this CAPT stuff, and everyone just suddenly moved to another state? What if there was some kind of mass exodus just so no one had to take the CAPT? What would the head honchos at the capital do then?

If we were to look at the broader picture of things, we would see that CAPT practice extends way past the small segment we did in English class. This was not just some thing that came up in casual conversation a couple weeks before we took it. The system had been drilling this into our heads since sixth grade, and maybe even a little longer. They kept telling us, "You have to pass. Have to pass! *Have to pass!*" This statement was always immediately followed by, "I'm sure all of you will do fine."

So what did all of us do? Well, what do you think we did?! We freaked out! We didn't want to be stuck in this place any longer than we had to! It was a paranoia that spread like the plague.

STAGE 1—Denial: "This is nothing to worry about. We're a smart group of kids; we'll be okay. Everything is going to be okay, right? Right! It's all going to be perfectly fine...that's right, perfectly fine ..."

STAGE 2—Blame: "The state can't do this! This is so gay! Fuck! I hate this! Why the hell did they make this thing mandatory? Why did we have to be the first class? Why did I have to be born in Connecticut? My parents should have never come here! Oh fuck, I hate this!"

STAGE 3—Fear: "Holy shit, I have to pass this! How am I supposed to do this? I'm not smart! It's all writing? Shit! I was never good at writing stuff. They can't expect me to be able to do all this! I'm gonna fail this so bad, I have no idea what I'm doing, I'm gonna be stuck here forever…shit, shit, shit, shit!"

STAGE 4—Acceptance: "Well, I guess I have no choice in the matter. There's nothing I can do but to just go in and take it. Deep breaths, deep breaths…Shit; this is going to suck ass!"

Certainly our descriptive vocabulary leaves something to be desired. Then again, there may be wherein our talent lies. When I was in middle school, I thought the word "fuck" was just a bad swear. Once I got to high school, I learned that it could be so much more. I've seen people use it as a noun, a verb, an adjective, an adverb…conjunction, prepositional phrase, and just about everything else. It may not sound pretty, but you've got to admire their effort.

So after week after week and year after year of preemptive learning, we finally sit down to take this reprehensible test. Anticipations were high, hopes were low, self-esteem was low, standards were low…a lot of things were low. The good news was that if we failed any part of it this time around, we would be able to take it again during our junior year. The bad news was…y'know, now that I think about it, the good news in and of itself was the bad news, too. None of us were really consoled by the idea of having to take the damn thing over again.

CAPTain! We're Breaking Up!

If at first you don't succeed, destroy all evidence that you have tried.

—Rule of Failure

One of the first bits we did was called "Interdisciplinary Writing." For sixty-five minutes, you read three articles about a certain topic, and then you write a letter to whoever gives a shit for or against the topic. They're all pretty much trivial subjects. You do this not once, not twice, but *three* times! The first one we had was about whether or not private companies should be allowed to advertise in schools. A pointless argument, since it is inevitable. Advertisers can't be stopped in this aspect, so why waste your breath? The next one was on whether or not juveniles should be tried as adults. If you cared (and most didn't), I suppose it could go either way. That's the thing about these persuasive letters—you don't persuade anybody to your point of view. You pick whichever side is easier to argue for. What good does that do? The third one, and Buddha only knows why we had to do yet another one of these, was about whether or not online education is good or bad. Why? Why the fuck bother? You can't change it, and you certainly can't stop it! What's next? "Should penguins be kept in zoos? New studies show that yes, yes they should."

Then there was "Responses to Literature." In other words, we get to enjoy the work of some two-bit author who can't get published anywhere else who's making up stories for heroin money as opposed to getting a real job. That's just great. We read one about some fat girl who everybody hated, and by the end of it, I hated her, too. I did get a cheap laugh when the story described how she dealt with her depression by (metaphorically) crawling deep inside herself, as if she was a cave. Does anyone else see the irony in a fat chick wanting to "crawl inside herself"?

After we read the story, we had to answer four questions about it. These were mostly of the "How do you feel about ...?" variety. The first one was, "What did you think about this story?" Well, let me take a quick trip to the bathroom, and I'll show you what I thought about it! The second dealt with explaining a quote from the selection. I hate to sound pompous about this (even though I'll probably come off as such anyway), but I could have pulled better quotes from this allegory. And this thing didn't even have a purpose, let alone a story line. The third one was, "What was this story's theme? You may relate it to your own life experiences, other books, movies, etc."

I did good on that one: "The theme of finding oneself has been shown in such books as *The Suicide Club* by Ron Burns and in movies such as Kevin Smith's cult comedy classic, *Clerks*." I don't think they bought either of those. The final question was, "In your opinion, how successful do you think the author was in creating a good piece of literature?" Oh man, that was a splendid one.

Using my superb writing skills and the best of my thinking faculties, I ripped the author a new asshole. Damn straight.

We did another section that was similar to this one, only with multiple choice questions and shorter stories. Those weren't much better. How would you like to read the story of Hemoheb, the little Egyptian who dreams of becoming a scribe? Yeah, didn't think so. Hemoheb? What the hell? I know this stuff isn't supposed to be the most exciting material in the world to begin with, but you guys aren't even trying anymore. Come to think of it, we did a lot of testing that involved reading one kind of article or another. One of them was on how Tiger Woods is revolutionizing the world of sports. My immediate reaction was, "No, he's not." Actually, my immediate reaction was my gag reflex, but that was my first thought. There are very few incidents where I've really felt like I've squandered my time in this world, but writing about that was definitely one of them. When I talked to Kate later that day, I thought she was going to have an ulcer. She completely flipped out. "Tiger Woods *sucks*! Golf *sucks*! That whole article *sucked*!" She doesn't swear too often, but her rage limits her vocabulary just the same.

Then there was the article on alternative forms of transportation. Y'know, because we're going to run out of fossil fuels in a few thousand years, so we'd better stop driving cars before it's too late. That one actually quoted some tree-hugger—excuse me, environmentalist—who was quoted as saying, "Cars are likely to be the predominant form of ground transportation in the near future, and probably longer." No shit. You see? That was unnecessary. All you have to say is "in the future." That's all that's needed to get the point across. Dumbass.

After the first day, we were completely fried. After putting my pencil down, I realized that if we wrote this much day after day of testing, our hands were going to be completely deformed by the end of it. Thinking aloud, I sarcastically stated, "Wow, that was exciting."

The voice of Bri came from the desk in front of me: "Yeah! I got a natural high off of that!"

If the writing parts didn't phase you, then the math parts would. Currently, there's some bizarre law in Connecticut that prevents students from being tested before nine o'clock. So the math exam—all three hours of it—started at nine in the morning and went straight through noon. Kids who were used to eating at a little after twelve were now eating around quarter after one. It was bad enough that we were made to suffer through all of the testing, but now we have to be starved, too? Well, at least we got a fifteen-minute break with Teddy Grahams in between the two sessions. That almost made the whole thing endurable. Almost.

Then—last, but not least—was the science section. Wait, I take that back—it was the least. It was the easiest test I had ever taken in my life. Yes, even easier than that quiz on shapes that we took in kindergarten. There was an essay question that showed a picture of a girl playing soccer, and beneath it was the statement, "The girl shown is using energy to kick the soccer ball that originated from the sun. Describe how this happened." As far as explanations go, this one takes the scenic route. I'm not quite sure what I accomplished by writing it. The state seems to think we've got something to prove. That was another complaint that I had about the test—the huge amount of racist sectionalism. Since this was an aptitude test for Connecticut, every question on the practice tests had something, *something* to do with maple syrup. By the time they were asking me how much sap it takes to make four quarts of concentrated syrup, I was exceptionally pissed.

All of this had to be done whilst listening to those select few juniors (who did not have to pass in order to graduate from high school) among us going off in between testing periods: "Well I failed that! Did you fail that? Shit, I completely bombed it. I'm so glad I don't have to pass this thing…"

At the very end, at the very back of our test booklets, was a survey. There were about seven or eight questions, followed by a list of responses that ranged from "Strongly Disagree" to "Strongly Agree." I don't need any more invitation to wreck havoc than this:

"I found the articles interesting."

Strongly disagree.

"The charts and graphs greatly helped me in writing my article."

Strongly disagree.

"I found the Interdisciplinary Writing section difficult."

... Undecided. It's clearly a trick question, because if you tell them it's easy, they'll make it harder next year. And if you tell them it was hard, then they'll still make it harder...which I guess makes it more of an ultimatum than a double-dealing interrogatory.

If you were of the Utopian mindset, you would probably say that the CAPT testing built character. If you are of more realistic thinker, as am I, you might write the whole thing off as a colossal waste of time, or even go as far as to say that it's just one more example of what is so fundamentally wrong with public school systems in latter years. More and more, I find myself in neither camp. I think I've finally accepted the idea that the whole mess was one giant stepping-stone in the ever-deepening pool of bureaucracy. A sense that elected officials have lost touch with the last remnants of reality. Said Mr. Denis on the subject, "I was talking with some of the last few friends that I have in the State Legislature from my years as Mayor (of our town) about CAPT testing. And we argued back and forth, and finally I said, 'Well, since you're making kids take the CAPT in order to pass high school, then it's only fair that you take the CAPT test, too. If you don't pass, you have to step down from office.'...None of them agreed to it."

Other English Beguilement

Every year, Mr. Denis assigns one major paper on an author. This year, I asked if I could do myself. His reply? "It has to be an author who has gained public recognition." Dammit! That would have been so easy! Well, I can try again next year. I don't mind reports that much, as most of the time I can write an entire narrative from prior knowledge. My secret? Old episodes of *Wishbone*. You are free to laugh at the idea all you want, but that's how I taught myself classical literature—everything from *A Tale of Two Cities* to *The Hound of the Baskervilles*. When time comes to pay the piper, it's the other kids who are the ones asking me for summaries and advice. All it takes is a half-hour of PBS for six months, and you're there.

Serena did not fair as well. In an e-mail she sent me a few days before the first of several dates on which drafts were due, she notified me of her discontentment: "GOD I HATE ENGLISH...WHAT A WASTE OF MY LIFE!" Yeah, she wound up writing it eventually. In fact, she wrote about twice as much as I did. But that didn't mean she had to like it. Analytical reports seem to be a thorn in the side of her sanity. "This report is so gay! Why do we have to write about what other people think?" She was venting most of her rage at me because I'm one of the few people she talks to in this class by choice.

"Do you really want me to answer that, or do you want to keep bitching?"

I don't think she realized that it was a rhetorical question. "I want to keep *bitching*!"

Josh wasn't too happy about the endeavor, either. Not that I helped any. "Stefan! Do you know anything about the works of Sherlock Holmes?"

I answered with a calm sense of derision, "Well, Josh, I don't. You see, Sherlock Holmes was a fictitious character. Now, if you're asking me if I know anything about the works of Sir Arthur Conan Doyle, I might be able to help you out." It's alright—he knows I'm just joshing him...It's a horrible pun, I know, but in the end, I decided to go with it anyway.

The paper was assigned about a month in advance. That wouldn't be too bad if it wasn't for the intermediate deadlines that Mr. Denis gave us. Drafts, drafts, and more drafts. I hate drafts. I despise drafts—I *loathe* drafts. He told us that he wanted us to get started on our projects so that we would have an idea on where we were heading with them. So I asked him, "What's the difference between finding out where we're heading now, or, let's say, the day before it's due?" I got a few light laughs from around the room, but not the answer I was hoping for. Then I went ahead and did a draft the way I wasn't supposed to (unbeknownst to me).

"I was expecting paragraphs," he said.

"Well, I kinda met you halfway on that."

"Yeah, that's kinda what I did with your grade, too." Ouch. I walked right into that one. Damn, I usually see those coming.

The lot of us are careful in our grouching, as Mr. Denis is not nearly as bad when it comes to assignments as some of the other English teachers (who, for all intents and purposes, shall remain unidentified). Though we don't always show it, we are more than grateful to be in this English class. More than once, we have been ridiculed and cursed by other students who were not among the fortunate few to have him as a teacher.

If you ever wanted to know how good you had it here, and how bad it was elsewhere, you need to look no further than Luke. He was one of those who had to go through the trials and tribulations of much more strenuous learning environments. In the morning discussions before homeroom, he would, on occasion, become a kind of standup comedian. The others would gather 'round him so that they might hear the latest rants and raves that he had to share, his subversive, low-toned voice breathing the fire and brimstone of the modern age.

"So I met with (the teacher) this morning. I had a play that had to be underlined, a short story that had to be underlined, and another short story that had to be in quotes. How the fuck was I supposed to know that? ...

"She said I had to shorten the title. I'm like, 'It's three fuckin' words!'

"Basically, she called me stupid and ripped my paper apart...(In mimicry) 'I know you worked really hard on this, but it sucks ass!'"

His sentiments spoke to many others who were suffering the same treatment. Those of us who had Mr. Denis and were there at the time stood abashed and closemouthed throughout.

But besides the papers, the CAPT practice, and all the other things that were detestable about English class, there was a lot of good in it. There were things that we enjoyed. Things that we took pride in. We did skits, including one on Robert Frost's poem, "Stopping By Woods On A Snowy Evening." We went all-out on that one, with special effects (to this day, Josh insists that we needed a stronger fan) and death on guitar. The latter of which made it seem more like "Stopping By Woods On A Snowy Evening In Mexico," but I can live with that. So long as Antonio

Banderas wasn't involved. We read poems aloud, had the chance to read creative stories, inventive letters, original poems. We actually had the chance to be original, instead of being drilled with grammatical and literary nonsense. One of my favorite pieces of all time was the script to a dialogue between Laotzu and a contemporary high school student, which Serena and I then had the chance to perform in front of the class.

A CONVERSATION BETWEEN
LAOTZU
&
A CONTEMPORARY HIGH SCHOOL STUDENT
WRITTEN BY STEFAN KOSKI

LAOTZU—STEFAN
CONTEMPORARY HIGH SCHOOL STUDENT—SERENA

(Laotzu is seen sitting on a desk, meditating. Contemporary High School Student enters from stage left.)

CONTEMPORARY HIGH SCHOOL STUDENt: Hi, are you…*(having difficulty with the name)* Laotzu?

LAOTZU: Are you with the Internal Revenue Service?

CHSS: No.

L: Then yes, I am! Please, come in and sit, my child. *(She sits in chair in front of desk.)* You must be Sedina.

CHSS: Actually, it's "Serena."

L: The Way has many names, child.

CHSS: No really, it's "Serena."

L: Sedina, Serena—potato, potat-to. What is it that you seek?

CHSS: You, I guess. I heard you were the new guidance counselor, Laotzu.

L: Who told you my name?

CHSS: Umm, you did.

L: Oh, right. Yes, I am the one called "Laotzu." But please, call me "Louis."

CHSS: Sure…Louis. My friend has a problem.

L: Does this friend happen to be you?

CHSS: *(Hesitating)*…No.

L: Is she really a friend, or is she just an acquaintance?

CHSS: Uhh, I dunno.

L: But of course you don't know! *Knowing* is not what's important, it's *not* knowing.

CHSS: It is?

L: Yes! For example, do you *know* the solution to this problem?

CHSS: No.

L: And neither do I! That's my point!

CHSS: But you don't even know what the problem is!

L: Exactly.

CHSS:...Right. So my friend has this problem. She thinks that her boyfriend has been cheating on her, but she doesn't know who it might be.

L: You're asking the wrong question! The question is not "who," it's "why." Why has everything started falling apart in their relationship? Why was your friend targeted for this emotional conflict? Why was an assassination necessary this late in the administration? Who came between the two that caused this distance to materialize?

CHSS: I thought you said I'm not supposed to ask "who."

L: Well, just this once it's okay.

CHSS: So you're saying that I should try to figure out *why* things are going wrong instead of *who* is causing the problem?

L: Why must you be the one to resolve this conflict? You carry a heavy burden that I would not wish upon anyone. Well, almost anyone.

CHSS: Because that's what friends do! When the greatest of troubles engulf those who are closest to us, we must come to their aid and assist them! The mightiest of tribulations are never powerful enough to bring down the bond of—are you sleeping?

L: Hmm? Uhh, no, I'm just resting my eyes. Please, continue.

CHSS: That's it.

L: Oh, right. Why is it that this current relationship is the one that needs to be saved? Who was first?

CHSS: Well, Tom was first.

L: What was second?

CHSS: I guess Mike was second. I don't know who was third.

L: I thought you said "who" was first?

CHSS: No, Tom was what was first.

L: I thought you said "what" was second?

CHSS: *(Getting angry)* No! Mike was the one who was second!

L: But you said "who" was first!

CHSS: Tom was who was first; Mike was what was second!

L: Third base.

CHSS: Alright, look, are you going to help me, or not?!

L: Shhhh…easy, my child. The Way of the universe is mysterious and shrouded in dark, murky, black…stuff. The greatest of wisdom can only be gained through experience, and that is what your friend is getting right now. In time, she will be the one to figure out the truth of this man's nature. It's just like what I told Jimi Hendrix: You can't judge a book by its cover.

CHSS: You weren't the first one to say…Wait, you knew Hendrix?

L: Yes, we met at Woodstock. I told him, "Possessions are fleeting," and he stole my stash.

CHSS: You mean your stash of *wisdom*?

L: Riiiiight…"wisdom." Is that what you kids are calling it these days?

CHSS: Calling what?

L: Nothing. Listen, tell your friend to look deep within her being, to the very cockles of her heart. I think she will find the answer that both you and she seek. And if you have any further questions, be sure to consult my book, *The Tao Te Ching, Fifth Edition*. Now available on audio-cassette.

CHSS: I'll do that. *(Getting up to leave)* Thanks, Louis.

L: Think nothing of it, Serena…So, what are you doing Friday night?

CHSS: Don't you think it's a little weird for a guidance counselor to be asking a student out?

L: A guidance what now?

CHSS: I've gotta go. *(Walks away.)*

L: CALL ME!

Now and then, when I sit here, I take the time to look back on how this class has so profoundly impacted me, so incomparably changed me. If it wasn't for this, I may very well have lost faith in my writing capabilities. Perish the thought. I sit in my desk, trying to unscramble this one last damn sentence to gain a few extra points on my vocab quiz—"constantly my economic run and Canadians an those in juxtaposition away cows are the queen making are government seat of increasing causing the of crazy"—while Mr. Denis patrols the aisles to check on our progress, kicking my bag as he passes. It probably wasn't even in his way, but where else would he get his kicks (no pun intended) and giggles?

Once he returns to the front of the class, he crumples up a piece of paper and eyes the waste receptacle in the corner of the room. He turns his back on it, moving his arm in a throwing motion, constantly checking his position. Following the few fake throws, he looks at the class and asks, "How much do you want to bet that I can make it from here?" Serena offers a dollar; Josh, a Snapple. Then, with an impeccably deadpan tone, "A Snapple? Deal!" He prepares the throw, and then gently tosses it into a different trashcan, located directly in front of him. We should have seen it coming. With the devilish grin that he invariably gives whenever he fools anyone, he points to Josh and formally states, "You owe me one Snapple." Josh is in trouble now, because he's in the lunchroom at the same time that Mr. Denis is monitoring it.

Don't you worry; we got even with Mr. Denis, and gave him a taste of his own medicine. A few weeks later, standing on the opposite side of the room, with the trash can on the other side and another crumpled piece of paper in his hand, he asks us again, "Do you think I can make it?"

Josh was our unanimous spokesman in this one. "Do I think you can make a shot into *that* trash can, from *there*? No, I don't."

"What would you bet me?"

"How about we go double or nothing on that Snapple?"

"Double or nothing? That's too good to resist…The joke's on you, because I can make this shot anytime I want." So it seems that he's done this type of thing before. What was that old maxim? Ah yes, as an anonymous person once said, "The words you speak today should be soft and tender…for tomorrow, you may have to eat them." How true it is.

Mr. Denis lobs the ball of paper into the air. It arks high, then bounces off the wall. Smart thinking to use the wall as a backboard. But no, it ricochets off the wall, along the rim of the trashcan, and onto the floor. With that, the entire class, now having been awoken by the merrymaking, joins in the shouting of one long "OOOHHHHHHHHHH!!!" as was the custom at the time.

It's an odd kind of revelry in an otherwise dispiriting day. They all laugh at Mr. Denis's misfortune while I quietly laugh to myself as I imagine what would happen if that pile of old dictionaries on the shelf were to suddenly burst into flames. We sit content, anxiously waiting for the

RIIIIIIIIIIIINNNNNNNNNNNNNGGGGGGGGGGGGGGGG-GGGG!!!

… bell to ring. Dammit, I usually have much better timing. Ah well, now is not the time to be sorrowful about the responsive capabilities of my cerebral cortex. That can wait until math, for now, it is time to eat. I leave this chapter with one of my most cherished pieces of pseudo-literature. It follows the classic styling of a Romance tale ("Romance" not in the sense of a love story, but rather of deriving from the Roman language).

What is a classic Romance tale? It involves several basic elements: a hero, a quest, and a clash between good and evil in which good always prevails (for example, the tales of King Arthur). And to that extent, I follow the format very closely. In other regards, such as conventionality, perhaps not so much. It is, though, without a shadow of a doubt, the centerpiece jewel in a crown that is my final year of a halfway decent English class.

AN EXCERPT FROM THE
TALES OF MORRIS
BY STEFAN KOSKI

Who was Morris? Had you asked this question years ago, perhaps not even Morris would be able to tell you. Was he ambitious? Yes, yes he was. Was he eager for adventure? Yes, he undoubtedly was. Could he have predicted the events that were about to unfold and forever change his life? No, probably not.

Then again, some might say that it was inevitable. Morris, whose full name was Morristan Iris Kinley Estabala (his mother's idea, not his father's), was constantly getting himself into trouble. When he was six, he led a large group of boys in a violent riot that nearly burned the local schoolhouse to the ground. They say "nearly" because the materials used in the attack turned out to be not quite as flammable as Morris had hoped. He reportedly had his second-in-command executed for the blunder. When he was eleven, he murdered three of the seven village elders during an attempted coup d'etat to seize power. It would have worked, had not the other four rallied a resistance force at the precise moment. The battle that ensued destroyed Morris's local power base that he had spent years building up. As a result, the young Morris was banished forever. For the next ten years, he wandered aimlessly from kingdom to kingdom, begging and stealing to make a living.

In that regard, the masses can be forgiven for speculating that Morris was not all that he was cracked up to be. But in time, all things pass. He gained a reputation for being a skilled fighter, and distinguished himself on the field of battle several times during the great Oshkoshkan Civil War, where he fought as a mercenary for the royalists. It is rumored that he saved King Dom Jolly's life during an assassination attempt by diving in front of him whilst an arrow was fired. Some believe this, but others say that he had merely tripped and fell in front of the arrow's path. Regardless, several months after King Dom Jolly was restored to power, he summoned Morris to a conference at the capital city of Tolemac.

Morris was nervous about the encounter. He didn't trust kings. He didn't trust elders. For the most part, he did not trust anyone who was in power, because of all the people who did have power, he was not one of them. He was walking down a series of corridors of the king's inner chambers, a place that he had never been down before. The palace guards on either side of him were making him uneasy. After what seemed like forever, they arrived at a large set of double doors, on which an inscription read, "Caution: Door Opens Automatically." And with that, the doors did open automatically, a feature that only the wealthy landlords and 7-11 owners could afford. On a grossly oversized throne sat a tall, well-built man in his mid-thirties. Upon entering, the king rose to his feet, and a nearby page proudly announced, "All hail, King Dom Jolly III, lord of the midlands, emperor of the western colonies, supreme ruler of all peoples in the lands of Oshkoshkans, all-mighty head honcho of the blah blah blah...you get the idea."

Morris knelt very briefly (for the sake of keeping up appearances), before stating, "My Lord King Ruler Guy, I am honored." The king addressed Morris with a warm and genial tone, "Please, call me DJ. I have summoned you for a very important quest. Do you know what the SK-721 is?"

"A muffler part for a '79 Pinto?"

"No, but good guess. It is, in fact, the serial number of a book."

"What kind of book?" Morris asked inquisitively.

"Perhaps I should explain in further detail," the king stated solemnly, as he walked across the room to the large fireplace, staring into its glowing embers. "The book was lost many years ago, or it might have been stolen. At any rate, it contained the last teachings of Buddha, before he was murdered by the Imperial Guards of Emperor Tycaundra."

"Wait, you don't mean the..."

"I do. It is the fabled Tome of Stefanism, which supposedly contains the secrets to the science of gunpowder and other explosive weaponry. With this kind of knowledge and technology, one would be able to conquer the world! Don't you see it? I want you to recover the Tome so that Tolemac may conquer its many enemies, and unite the lands into one kingdom."

"What's in it for me?" Morris asked bluntly.

"In return for your services, I will pay you two hundred pounds of gold and give you an all expense-paid cruise to the Caribbean."

"Sounds good; I'm in."

"But I must warn you, the journey will be fraught with many perils and dang—"

"Hey! I said 'I'm in!' What more do you want?"

"Nothing more than the Tome, I assure you. To aid you in your quest, I am putting my most trusted lieutenant under your command. He will navigate you to the place where we believe the Tome is being held." With this, the king called out, "Jim, you may enter." A small man, not more than four feet in height, approached Morris and introduced himself in his own odd kind of way.

"Top o' the mornin' to ye', Marty! How beath yourself?" he asked, in the heaviest Irish accent allowed by the Writers Guild of America.

"The name's 'Morris.'"

"Whatever your name be, blue eyes, it not matters to me. I be Jim, and I'll be leadin' ya to the Tome."

"Great. Just great. The king's most trusted lieutenant is a wise-cracking leprechaun."

With this, the two set out from Tolemac to find the legendary Tome of Stefanism, a book that could forever change the world with its long-lost text.

* * *

The two did not speak until they reached the main road leading out into the countryside. It was Morris who broke the silence. "Where exactly is this Tome?"

"Aye, it be in the Temple of the Lost Souls. A land where no man ever dares to set foot."

"Well, of course not. I wouldn't want to go there either, with a name like that."

The two traveled on for many days, always heading north by northeast, aided only by the stars, Jim's keen sense of direction, and mapquest.com. One day, while passing through a meadow, they came upon three men fighting off a group of bandits. Jim and Morris helped the men kill the thieves, after which Morris introduced himself.

"Wassup? I'm Morris, and this is Jim. Who are you?"

The jacked warrior greeted the two with a wide grin and a deep voice typical of warrior types. "Aye, I be Sir Lancelot, and these be my two brothers, Sir Sleepsalot and Sir Eatsalot. We thank you for your help with those dirty scoundrels. Where are you off to?"

"We're on a journey to recover the Tome of Stefanism. Would you like to join us?"

"Not really, but since the plot of this story hinges on our decision, we'll come anyway."

And so it was that Morris, Jim, and the three knights of Tolemac journeyed on. At last, they reached the Temple of the Lost Souls. Creeping through miles of dark, dank caverns, they came to the shrine that held the Tome of Stefanism, the last teachings of Buddha. Morris was about to run and grab it when a massive two-headed dragon arose in front of them! Morris called out, "Jim! What the hell is this thing?!"

"Aye laddie, that be the Olsen Twins!"

"The *what*?!"

"The Olsen Twins! A fierce, two-headed dragon that legend says guards the Tome! The only thing worse than its bite is its mediocre acting career!"

"Holy mother of pearl," Sir Sleepsalot cried out, "it's hideous! And it shrieks with a power that could shatter glass!"

"There's only one way to slay such a foul beast!" Morris stated. And with that, he took a small flask that he had been saving for the occasion.

Jim spoke in a hoarse whisper to the others, "Only the freshly fallen dew of the sacred mountains would give a man the strength to kill such a beast." The other three gasped in astonishment. "It can't be. It couldn't be!"

"It is!" Lancelot shouted. "It's a flask of Mountain Dew Code Red!" Morris downed the mixture and roared with a loud voice, "DO THE DEW!!!" Instantly, he was infused with the strength of twenty men and slew the beast with ease. Morris, triumphant, took the mystical book from the pedestal and exited the cave with the others. They were at last on their way back to Tolemac.

* * *

It was a long three weeks back through the wilderness to the capital city. On their way, they encountered many people, both friend and foe. Their adventures were so numerous, and the author is so lazy, that all of them couldn't possibly be mentioned here (at this point in time). When they were about a day's journey from the city, the five were walking through the forest when Morris suddenly halted them. Something was different.

Something was...strange, somehow. Then, it hit him. "AMBUSH!" They drew their weapons, but the men carefully hidden in the trees were upon them before they could even put up a fight.

The leader of the crew approached the group. "Beath thou whom?"

Morris gazed at the man curiously. "I'm sorry, I didn't quite catch that."

The leader looked upon Morris with a hint of frustration. "My apologies. My lysdexia must be kicking in again. What I meant to say was, 'Who beath thou?'"

"I am Morris, and this is Lieutenant Jim and three of the king's knights—Sir Lancelot, Eatsalot, and Sleepsalot. We were on our way back to Tolemac."

"Tolemac?!" the crew leader replied. "The city of Tolemac is under siege! We were on our way to liberate it. Would you like to join us?"

"Not really," Morris replied, "but since the plot of this story hinges on our decision, we'll come anyway. Onward, men! We march on the capital!"

* * *

The next morning was cold and somber. A damp fog hung in the air. Morris, now General Morris, stood on a ridge overlooking the vast city. He was going over every last detail of the assault, carefully mulling over every facet of the attack. Jim quietly approached him. "So, laddie, what beath on ye' mind? Are you ready for this?"

"I'm not thrilled with the concept," Morris admitted with a sigh, "but I know it is a necessary evil that I must deal with. What do you think, Jim?"

Jim gazed on the city, which now glistened in the light of early dawn. "Me? Aye, I think that the end justifies the means, and that's something that you've got to live by." A strange silence fell between the two, both contemplating their fates.

"Are the men ready, Jim?" Morris finally asked.

"They're as ready as they'll ever be...Morris."

"Excellent. Prepare for the attack."

And at that moment, it started to rain.

* * *

Two thousand men, including two cavalry divisions and one flank of archers, stood awaiting orders, completely soaked from the downpour. Their expressions were filled with anticipation, their hands greedily plying the hilts of their swords. Morris, along with the other knights, led the march. They stopped at a small hillock. Before them was an open field, on which stood a large force of Emperor Hijan, the great-great grandson of Emperor Tycaundra, the emperor who had murdered Buddha so many years ago. The Imperial forces started marching toward them. Morris barked instructions to his men. "Archers ready!" Five hundred nervous hands strung their bows with freshly sharpened arrows, waiting for the next order. Morris gave it to them. "LOOSE!" The twang of the bows could be heard all around, the hiss of the arrows as they sang through the air.

Several of the Imperial guards fell, but the rest went from a walk to a trot, and then into a full run, yelling and screaming bloody murder as they went. Morris, more nervous than he had ever been in his life, then gave the last command that anyone could hear for the remainder of the engagement: "Ready! *Charge*! Fight for glory! Fight for honor! FIGHT FOR TOLEMAC!"

* * *

The battle was a three-hour affair that resulted in many casualties (of course), but near the end, Lancelot lead a cavalry charge that ultimately saved the day. Later that evening, King Dom Jolly sat in his throne room commending Jim, Lancelot, and his brothers for their bravery and courage. He bestowed upon them the highest of all honors, promoting all of them to the rank of Really, Really Awesome General. Turning to Lancelot, he asked, "Sir Lancelot, whatever became of Morris?"

"It's strange that you ask, sire. He was caught up in the heat of the battle, and we lost sight of him. Afterward, we never found his body, *nor did we find any trace of the Tome ...*"

* * *

NOTES FROM THE AUTHOR (Stefan Koski): For the curious mind, it should be noted that "Tolemac" is "Camelot" spelled backwards. I have included this story here on the recommendation of fellow students who believed it should be published. Without question, the story loses some of its intuitive charm by being simply being in printed text, as a story such as this deserves to be read aloud (preferably by a talented storyteller capable of reproducing a thick Irish accent). Some question whether or not the exceptionally short tale loses its objectivity at certain given points, to which I respond that it was very, very late when I was writing it (not that it had any objectivity to begin with). Only minor changes have been made between the version shown here and the original version that I read in front of my sophomore English class.

This new approach to a Romance tale brings up the ever-debatable concept of whether or not classic literature is still prevalent in today's society. While I am pressed to leave this decision up to the reader, it is notable that this particular tale puts a new spin on the standard Romance myth by adding elements of humor and pop culture to make it as relevant as possible, such as the Olsen Twins (a couple of mediocre actresses), Dom Jolly (host of *Trigger Happy TV*), Oshkosh (a clothing company), and 7-11 convenience stores. However, others, such as the names of Tycaundra, Hijan, and Morris himself, are simply whims of the author's imagination. And to be fair, I did steal that '79 Pinto bit from *Airplane 2*.

Miscellaneous Philosophy — Part 5
Televised Wasteland

Who Wants To Be A Millionaire? has got to be one of the worst shows ever created. It used to be somewhat decent until they started getting lots of stupid people on it. I saw one episode in which no one walked out with more than a thousand dollars. The questions weren't even difficult. I saw one guy from Utah get the question "In 1858, what was the predominant crop in the south with the label of 'King'? A. Wheat; B. Tobacco; C. Cotton; D. Corn."

He was so clueless that he had to use his 50-50 lifeline. Here was a guy who had probably been on this Earth for at least twenty years longer than me, probably attended college for several years, who just used a lifeline on a question that I learned the answer to yesterday during my history class. He got another question wrong later on, and wound up with $100. That's it! Hell, if he had just gone to work that day he would have made more! Eventually, they'll get to the point where they'll ask some really pathetic question and the jackass who's on will still need help. "What color is the sky? A. Red; B. Green; C. Blue; D. Magenta."

He'll stall and stall, "Hmmm...uhhh...geez, this is a tough one...hmmm..." Let's go to a commercial! They'll come back, and he'll still be there, "Hmmm...uhhh...I dunno...I'd like to use a lifeline. I'd like to call God." The phone picks up and a booming voice shouts, "It's 'C,' dumbass!"

Next question: "In 1954, the United States signed a trade agreement with which of the following: A. Japan; B. China; C. Russia; D. The Teletubbies."

"Okay, let me think...I guess it would be...hmmm...I'd like to use a lifeline. I'd like to call my Uncle Jim." He calls him up and a voice at the other end replies, "Dude, it's 'D'! It was the purple one!"

Chapter Eight

Lunch

Food is an important part of a balanced diet.
—Fran Liebowitz

Rejoice and be glad! For now the time has come to feast and be merry! The intermediate lunch waves (four in all) that will take place over the course of the next eighty minutes are a time for us all to recuperate, relax, and socialize with friends and countrymen. But mostly friends, definitely. Of course, for some, the suffering has only just begun. You see, because of the lunch waves, whatever class you have during that period is thirty-five minutes longer than usual. Some might have to deal with biology for an extra thirty-five minutes. Or even worse, how would you like to sit through geometry for an hour and twenty minutes?

Our cafeteria is not a very large room by any standards, but it serves the purpose that it was designed for. It's a very territorial environment. If there was ever a place where you felt the social factions were so well defined and out in force, this was the place. I ate in the cafeteria during my freshman year for the first quarter (first half of the first semester). After that point, I stopped for both germaphobic (fear of germs) and anthropophobic (fear of people) reasons. It seems that the wrestling team practices in the cafeteria. And the way in which they do it is that they run around, run, run, and run some more, wrestle, and do a variety of other things that would make one sweat profusely. Then they roll the mats up *without* cleaning anything. Then, at the next practice, they take all their stuff out again, and *then* they clean it. Once you hear about this, every time you sit eating in the cafeteria during the winter

125

sports season, you're constantly thinking about how you're eating among fermented wrestler sweat. From that point on, I never ate in the cafeteria again.

So where do I eat? Funny you should ask, because there's a rather lengthy and uneventful story surrounding that topic that I will now use in order to kill time and waste more space in an effort to make it seem like this book has some substance to it in the hope of getting published. For years—five of them to be exact—I was in band. It started in fourth grade, and continued right up through middle school. I played the trumpet. I was going to play the drums, but there were already a bunch of kids who had their hearts set on drums, and quite frankly, I wasn't cool enough for them (both the drums and the kids). The trumpet was the next-easiest instrument, because it only has three valves to push. If I were to pick up a saxophone or something, I wouldn't even know where to start. I played trumpet through middle school, even though I sucked, because if you didn't take band when you were in middle school, you had to take either chorus or general music. That was just how the system worked, and as far as I know, how it still works. I didn't know a lot at that point in my life, but what I did know was that both chorus and general music sucked even worse than band. They sucked *ass*.

When I was at the point that I was filling out my course selection sheet in order to pick my classes for my freshman year of high school, I saw no reason why I shouldn't continue taking band. Sure, I sucked, but how bad could band be? Yup, those were my famous last words. I might as well have entitled this book *Bigger than Jesus* after saying that. It still wouldn't have been as bad. I go to band in high school, and it sucked even more ass. It sucked more ass than the assiest ass sucker could ever suck. And let me tell you, that it is a *lot of ass*! After two weeks, I started looking into dropping it.

So I went to my local guidance department. That was mistake number one—I actually went to my high school guidance department expecting to receive guidance. That's all right, though. I realize now that I was an idiot for doing that, I've accepted it, and I can move on now. There are two guidance counselors, both guys named "Mike" (I told you there were too many "Mikes" in this school.) I like to think of them as some kind of wacky, offbeat group of superheroes whose comic book could never get published.

FASTER THAN A TAX RETURN!
MORE POWERFUL THAN BUDDHA!
THE ADVENTURES OF
GUIDANCE MEN!
BRAVELY FIGHTING EVERY FORM OF CONFUSION AND
STUPIDITY—INCLUDING THEIR OWN!

That's how I saw them, anyway. I even made up a logo for them. I'll have to show it to you some time. Each guidance counselor takes roughly half the alphabet by last name. I got Mr. K–Z, Mr. McGowan. He's the new guy, fresh from college but not without a sense of humor. He sits in his chair upright at all times, hair neatly cut, tie perfectly straight and aligned with his shirt, shoes spic-and-span, pants ironed almost to perfection. Jen reportedly had a crush on him at some point. But from what I know of Jen (which, admittedly, is way more than what I would like to know), that isn't all too surprising.

I told Mr. McGowan that band was on the fritz, and that I needed to take a different class. But because of the abnormal length of fifth period, all that was available were study halls. No good, because I needed the credit so that I could be a sophomore next year. It appeared that all hope was lost, which is typically the feeling that everyone gets after visiting guidance. It was time to use my B plan. Being a pessimist, I usually don't have a B plan—most of the time I generally assume that if my A plan doesn't work, I'm screwed. But this time, for reasons that are unknown to me even to this day, I had a B plan. And quite unexpectedly enough, it involved the girls' volleyball coach.

For all thoroughgoing functions, I have always referred to the coach as "Coach," so I will do the same here. I know Coach through my sister. My older, more talented, continually annoying sister. She was what you would call an overachiever. She played a total of four instruments: flute, clarinet, saxophone, and piano (in addition to dabbling in piccolo and French horn). During her four years of high school, she played three varsity sports, the largest portion of talent being focused in volleyball. Sooner or later, we met (her Coach and I, not my sister). Connect the dots. As soon as I entered my freshman year of high school, I was recruited to be a manager for the girls' volleyball team. Being the man of wit and intellect that I am, I should have probably seen that coming. Without going too much into detail, that's also how I signed away the next four years of my life. They always said that I could have quit, and I always said, "Yeah, right." Every once in a while, someone asks me if I'm still managing the team next year. I always give a small chortle, because there isn't any realistic way to get out of it, save death.

If the system has taught me anything, it's that there are a lot of rules. If Coach has taught me anything, it's that there aren't any rules. Or at the very least, there are ways around them. She tells me there might be another class that I could get into, one that isn't listed. But there's a catch—someday, she's going to ask a favor of me. I'm going to have to do something for her, even if it seems…dammit! I knew there would be a *Godfather* cliché involved somehow! Without paying too much attention to the details, I agree. Starting Monday, I am officially an intern…in the Guidance Department.

What are the odds? Technically, I'm not doing any of the guidance work (and what a scary thought that would be if I was). I'm going to be the assistant athletic director. What fun. At least now I have a place to eat my lunch—in the office of the all-powerful and all-knowing athletic director, Mr. Michael Savo. It's times like these that make me wish there was a way for me to transmit sarcasm through print.

The Real Guidance Department

In any organization, there will always be one person who knows what is going on. This person must be fired.
—*Conway's Law*

As an intern in the guidance department, I take care of most of the conventional office tasks. Copies are made, phone calls taken, faxes sent. But it is not a laborious position. Not at all. Every day is aberrant in one way or another.

Right when I walk into the Guidance Suite—and that is what they call it—Savo (as he is addressed by all) heralds my arrival. "Here he is! The star of the show!" For the first two weeks of the internship, it kinda freaked me out. Not so much the phrasing, but the theme music (whose source I could never quite identify) that he sang afterward. After a while though, it was just another part of my day. My errant, atypical day.

Savo himself is large man, jovial on most days for no discernible reason. His sable hair matted down and haphazardly combed forward, he sits in an oversized office chair without a care in the world...except for maybe when lunch is coming. Almost all of his shirts are Packers shirts, and keeping true to his sportsmanlike faith, an entire wall of his is filled with Packers paraphernalia—framed covers of newspapers from when they won the Superbowl, pictures of Savo at the Superbowl, and not the least of them, a Packers towel draping from one of the dusty shelves, filled with books that haven't been used since God knows when.

The office itself is nothing special. Melancholy, lamentable blinds cover the room's only window, which looks out onto a filing cabinet inhabiting a spot directly in front of it. One of the overhead lights has long since burned out, and the likelihood of it being replaced anytime in the near future is slim to nil. A commiserable desk stands against the wall, covered with useless items that no one has had the heart or the sense to throw out. A pitiful fan blows a halfhearted breeze across the chamber even though the enclosure is air-conditioned. It's sad, dismal...and strangely guidance-like.

I sit in the innermost corner of the room. Why? That's just how I operate. That's my spot, that's where I sit—end of discussion. And if someone's sitting in my seat, guess what? They're going to have to move. This is one of the few places where I am the superior in control. That's the thing about this business— being an intern here is like being in a gang, only with slightly less violence involved. Once you're in, they can't let you out because you know too much. At this point, I've already been endowed with more knowledge than what should be allotted to anyone.

Beyond saying that, I am not at liberty to disclose any further details.

Just as I'm sitting down to eat lunch, Karri walks in. Like most of the people who regularly hang around guidance, she's a senior. She's a four-year veteran of the volleyball team, with her out-standing jumping capabilities making up for her relatively small frame. She was a freshman here when my sister was a senior (which, as a point of trivia, was also the year that the team came the closest to winning the state championship). Right away, you can tell that something is wrong. "Do you want to know what I got on my report card? Fifties across the board due to absences! Someone might not be graduating this year, and she is *not* happy about it!"

In this school, when you have five absences or more (or ten tardies or more), your grade automatically drops to a fifty. But judging by her current outrage, it would appear that she has already figured this out. She paces around the office, barraging Savo with inquiries as to how to fix it. You can't help but stand in awe of the kind of fire that she has. Sometimes I think that if I ever had a daughter, I think I would name her Karri. Actually, her full name would be Karri Katelyn Koski—just so I could have a kid with the initials KKK.

Savo has been expecting this news for weeks, as her physics grade hasn't been all that great. She has an unusual habit of fail-ing one class per year. Most of the time, she has been able to get by just fine, but alas, her practices have finally caught up with her. After briefly consulting Savo, she leaves in earnest to put up whatever efforts she can to keep from winding up in summer school. As most can tell you, summer school is a fate mildly worse than death.

She's been begging Savo to paint his office a different color (as a future interior-design major, the beige walls appall her) and to put something on the walls other than Packers baubles. That got shot down pretty quick. "No one is allowed to do any more redecorating in my office," he firmly asserted, as I tried to hide the smirk on my face. Yes, I'm the one who brought about this rul-ing. It happened when Jen became an intern here. How she did that, I don't know. When I got the news, I was stunned. Stunned and horrified. I never felt so...so...*violated.*

It got worse when she wrote on Savo's white board calendar (in big lettering), "Calendar by Jen, aka the BEST INTERN. HA HA Stefan!" That was the last straw. *Now, it was personal.* I devised a plan that took full advantage of my elaborate cruelty. I waited until the schedule was rotated to when she would be in guidance the period after I was in (I had insisted that we be put in at different time slots). Then, using Savo's computer (fortunately, he wasn't in that day), I typed up a flyer that said in large, boldface type, "Jen needs to get over herself." Ah yes, perfect. Then I made about fifty or sixty copies of it, and plastered Savo's office with them. And I mean I put them *everywhere*—walls, floor, ceiling, the whole bit.

Everything would now be set for when she came in next period. Do you know what the weird thing about it was? It took me all of period E to complete it, and both the school principal and Savo's secretary (both of whom walked in while I was preparing this devious prank) didn't bother to stop me. Strange. Regardless, she walked into the guidance suite at quarter of one unaware of what I had done. Unaware, that is, until the principal (in the suite at the time) pointed it out to McGowan. "Oh yeah, I noticed that," he said quietly to her.

"Noticed what?" Jen asked, as I eagerly waited for the reaction (that I knew was coming) just outside the room. She walks in, gasps, and shrieks in exasperation, *"Stefan!"* Yes! *Victory was mine!* But do you know what the best part was? McGowan made her clean up the entire office, and take down every last flyer. I almost fainted with joy, and laughed the hardest that I had laughed in a long time as I dashed out. Sure, there were a few of her closest friends who were pretty pissed, but the rest of my fellow classmates shared in my triumph. For weeks to come, I was commended, praised, high-fived, and applauded whenever I walked into a room where those who knew what had happened were present.

Moments of Introspection

Turning my attention to my lunch, I discover that I am missing my napkin. It's these little details, all the little things, that
most often ruin my day. I should have expected as much, considering that I had two napkins yesterday. My lunch itself has consisted of the same food items for years: a fluffer-nutter sandwich
on cinnamon-swirl bread, a Juicy Juice juice box, a meal replace-
ment bar, a Kudos bar, a Twix bar, and an apple. Furthermore, the
contents of my lunch are consumed in that order, every day. Is it
because a regular routine gives me comfort in an uncontrollable
and unpredictable environment? I don't know. I think it's just that
I've never found any plausible reason to change it. For whatever
reasons, my lunch seems to bring back a lot of old memories for
people. "Kudos bars? I used to love those things. I used to eat
them everyday." Or, "Fluffer-nutter sandwich? Those things are
great! I'm gonna make one when I get home." I'm not sure what
to make of the phenomenon. We could assume that it's because of
some traumatic experience from our childhood. But then again,
what isn't these days?

Just at that moment, Savo reenters his office (or rather, my
office) and informs me that Coach has requested an audience
with me. Not with those exact words of course, but something to
that effect. Coach is taking over for Savo as athletic director next
year, and it would seem that I am the one who is charged with
making sure that the transition runs smoothly.

I return, after a five-minute conference with her, completely
dumbfounded. It would seem that she wants to have every single
sports schedule for next year along with the contact information
for every person even remotely associated with sports in
Connecticut on a floppy disk, as soon as possible.

I was under the impression that nobody uses floppy disks
anymore (not for anything useful, at least), but I think that would
be a lost cause as far as arguments go. Besides this, it is, quite literally, impossible to perform this task. The schedules for spring
and most of the winter sports haven't even been decided yet. I
turn to Savo, exasperated. "Is she crazy?" A stupid question, I
know.

Savo responds with a bit of a knowing laugh, "Well, Kosk, we already knew that she was crazy! What were you expecting?" Good question. I'm not sure what I was expecting myself. No matter, I'll find a way around it. I think I'll just get a blank disk, remove some crucial part of it so that it doesn't work, and then give it to her. She's not computer savvy; she'll never know. She'll probably wind up losing it within days of getting it, anyway. Short cuts are more than an option in this business—they're a way of life.

While passing this motion for lower standards, the bell rings. The first lunch wave has now ended; the second begins. Yippee-yai-kai-yay. Soon after the bell rings, Kate walks in, and Savo steps out (to where, I haven't the foggiest of ideas). When I found out that Kate was moving at the end of the school year, I offered to let her visit Savo's office any time she wanted. She comes here during the second lunch wave instead of going to the cafeteria. That's right—I get to decide whom I want to bestow favors on. A few months prior, Savo was relatively unaware that she existed. Now she's like family. In recent times, she seems more and more like family to me. And I mean that in a good way, considering I don't really click with my immediate, biological family. She was like a daughter to me; I was like a brother to her; Coach and Savo thought we were a budding romance. Oh yeah, we were a regular Southern couple.

Taking a seat in Savo's large, comfy office chair, she exhales ever so slowly as she lays back in her best attempts to get comfortable, her blonde hair cascading down her ever-so-tense shoulders. There are happy moments in her life; I don't have any doubts about that. But every day just holds so many plights and predicaments for her, and I know from all the stories she's told me that things are rarely easy. I think she summed it up best when, after completing one such tale, she expressed with a sigh, "What a life I live." I think the same could be said for the lot of us. On really bad days, days when she's had to deal with sickness (which constantly plagues her overreached and overextended body), bitchy people, lack of sleep, lack of food, and a lack of kindness in general, I find myself filled with sympathetic thoughts. You can't help but wonder why this kid, so benign and generous in so many ways, has to suffer. All of this while, assholes like me pass through day-to-day life relatively unscathed. Why?

It's odd, in a way. Before me sits one of the few people I've genuinely been able to identify with. Here was someone who actually understood what it was like to walk through the Jaws of Hell, to challenge Fate, and to come out with her head held high. Finally, after so many years of being in limbo by comparison, I have found someone who has led me by example to the way that things should be. And now that that has happened at last, she's moving out of state. Now I know why I've always believed that optimism was just something people use to lie to themselves.

After talking with her for ten minutes (give or take, depending on the day), her track coach, Mr. Foulds, meanders in. He's not a particularly tall man, built like a tank with too much armor. They'll talk about track meets, track practices, and track workouts, which is to be expected of a conversation with a track coach. It's always fun to listen to them discuss the track workouts, since I never have the slightest clue what they're talking about. It's like a foreign language, and in some ways, it's worse than a foreign language. I at least understand some Spanish. The whole happening gives me vague flashbacks about when I did track, and you already know how I feel about flashbacks.

Ye Olde Track 'n' Field

Let's first make it clear that I am not a man of sports, or most kinds of exercise for that matter. A little bit of tennis now and then? Yes. Intensive training to vie in large competitions of physical exertion? No. So normally, I wouldn't even be a candidate for school sports. However, during my freshman year (of all times), Coach calls in that favor that I had (stupidly) promised her. Here I was, hoping that she had forgotten all that pledge and promise stuff, but no such luck. One of her friends is coaching track this year, and she wants me to join. Now granted, Coach had been on my ass to join a lot of different activities with the argument that I would be good at them, including soccer, basketball, wrestling, boys' volleyball (at another school), and the chess club (don't know what the hell she was thinking on that one). But this time she had me cornered with her reasoning skills, and I at last caved to demands. I tried to "Just Say No," and it didn't work, dammit! D.A.R.E. never told me what to do *after* I give into peer pressure!

I remember the first day of practice. I don't remember it like it was yesterday' more like I remember it like it was a week ago. I was standing in front of the door to the boys' locker room (which was locked — yeah, irony is a blast) with Mikey and his cronies, all of whom were trying out for baseball. Mikey looked at me, looked at my bag of gym clothes, and energetically and enthusiastically (as most of his speech is) asked, "Are you trying out for baseball?"

"No, track," came my solemn reply.

"Oh," he said.

Oh? Yes, "oh." It was not one of these, "Oh, you're trying out for a sport, best of luck to you on that" kind of "oh's," either. It was one of these, "Oh, I'm so sorry for you and that's why I sound like you're going to your own funeral" kind of "oh's." I might have expected as much, since track was never a cool thing to do. From as far as I can tell, it never will be. There's this simple idea that if you spend day after day running, jumping, and throwing stuff just for the sake of running, jumping, and throwing stuff, then you're wasting your life. I can't say, in all honesty, that I entirely disagree with that line of thought.

I went out to the track (the actual track *place*) with my mind set on doing long jump and high jump, since I (correctly) figured that jumping was the only thing that I would be good at. Well, I originally wanted to do the 100-meter dash, too, right up until the point where I actually tried to run the 100-meter dash. There were perhaps four of us, lined up at the starting point. We all shouted, "Go!" at the same time. For a little while, by which I mean several seconds, I was keeping pace with them. Around the thirty-meter mark, I started getting tired. At the fifty-meter mark, I was completely exhausted and out of breath. And that was the end of any hopes that I may have had of becoming a sprinter.

At the high jump and long jump, I fared much better. My technique gradually improved, and for a while, it looked as if I might even make Berkshires (the regional league championship for schools of our size and funding) for the long jump. Then, something quite unexpected happened. Our coach (a friend of Coach's and a relatively casual acquaintance of mine) had to coach the girls' junior varsity softball team (for reasons that we shall not thrash out). The former track coach from years past replaced her. That was the point at which things *took a turn*.

I remember the first track meet that our new coach—who was really the old coach, but was new to me—was in command. At this point in the game, I had already developed a strong and deep mistrust of track meets. Previously, at the first track meet of the season and the first track meet that I had ever participated in, the team and I journeyed to a school known as Northwestern. The key part of that name is the word "north," because it was like the north in every way that people conventionally think of northern places. It was cold. *Very cold.* Freezing cold, you might say. And even though it was already April, by the end of the track meet we were experiencing near-blizzard type conditions. There is no need to mention, then, that my first experience with a track meet was not pleasant.

Several weeks later, we were at this other track meet at home, up against the Lewis Mills and the Oliver Wolcott Tech high schools. My new coach did not think that I was jumping materi-al. So on that day, the day of the meet, he tells me that I'm going to do the three hundred-meter hurdles—an event that I had never done before, had never practiced for, and, for the most part, was-n't even fully aware of the existence of up until then. I went to our star hurdler, Asa, and asked him, "How do you do hurdles?" He was a little flabbergasted at the question. I anticipated this, since it was plainly obvious that I was asking him to explain the special art and technique that is required to do this event, the event that *he* had been perfecting over countless years, in a period of rough-ly five minutes. After his thorough elucidation, two key facts dawned on me. The first was that hurdling required me to lift my right leg into a position that I was not capable of lifting it to; and second, I would have to do a lot of running. As I already men-tioned, I am not very proficient at running.

I get up to the starting line with all the other hurdler people, most of whom were quite masterful athletes. The official tells me that I'm going to be running in the third heat. That's right, I'm not going to be running with the Class A hurdlers, or even the Class B—I'm going to be running with the Remedial hurdlers. Once it's my turn to go, I find myself getting increasingly nervous. Here I am, in front of a relatively large crowd and decent-sized group of kids, and they're all expecting me to jump over these massive barrier things like it's an Olympic event. No pressure though—it's not my fault that I suck at an event that I was never conditioned for, or even wanted to do.

BANG! The gun goes off and the people on either side of me fly like the wind! WHOOSH! I figure that the best way to run this will be to start off with a light jog, and then move into a slightly lighter jog. Now I don't know how to really move like a hurdler per se, but I do know how to run, and I do know how to jump over things. The optimal thing to do, then, is to take this thing one step at a time. I run to the first hurdle. Then I slow down, almost to a stop but not quite, in order to prepare for the jump. With the best of my ability put forthwith, I vault over the damn thing. Ladies and gentlemen, I give you the best of my assurances that it was not a pretty sight. People were laughing and deriding me for the rest of the track season for my terribly awkward leaping form, and people still laugh about it whenever it is brought up in conversation to this day.

Once I'm over the first one and my feet are back on the ground, I run to the second hurdle, and repeat the same gross vaulting gesture. After about two hundred meters of this, I am sucking wind and jogging the lightest jog I've ever jogged in my life. The other people who were running have already long since finished. Now a strange thing starts to happen. Everywhere along the final one hundred meters of track, people are cheering me on! Not just the select other members of my own team, but the entire crowd! They're up in the stands shouting, doing the wave, and rooting like the friggin' circus has come to town! Then I notice that kids on the other teams are screaming, "Go, Terryville! Yeah!" I thought, "This is great! I'm not even within earshot of winning, and I'm the star of the show!" Someone later told me that they all did it out of sympathy for me, and I told him to shut the hell up.

I cross the finish line, and the guy there, in an almost mournful voice, announces my time: one minute, three seconds. For those of you who are not familiar with all things track, that's pathetic to the point of being disturbing. By comparison, the time that was needed to make the Berkshire League Tournament was forty-five seconds. I told our hurdler star, Asa, my time, and he calmly told me in the best tone he could afford, "Wow, that's really...bad." You're damn right it is! What the hell was our coach thinking?! Of course, my coach—in his infinite wisdom—thought that my time would improve with practice. So he made me practice hurdles instead of my jumping events. During the last track meet of the season, I was doing a minute and fifteen seconds on the three hundred-meter hurdles, and my long jump distance fell about two feet from what it had been at my peak. I didn't even place in the high jump.

And after that whole charade, I told others, and myself, "Fuck! I'm never doing track again!" Even without the whole hurdler pretension, I still probably wouldn't have done track again. It was a waste of time and required way too much exercise. Besides, I had paid my debt to Coach. I am home free from here on in.

An Event Un-Foulds

It just so happens that while Kate and Foulds are having their own little powwow, Mr. Denis walks in. Kate and I can relate to Mr. Denis, since we are among the lucky few to have him for English this year. He strolls in, coffee in hand, and snidely remarks, "No staff to be found, kids everywhere...this must be Guidance." Right you are, Mr. Denis, right you are! He always seems to have an intrinsic ability to keep an absolutely straight face whenever he's talking about something, no matter how outrageous the subject may be. I talk to him about the English paper that's due soon (that I haven't done yet), and Kate will bring up the details of whatever kind of breakfast she's made for him recently. Yes, I didn't know that Kate made Mr. Denis breakfast, either, so you're in the same boat that I'm in—an old boat, with a broken motor, rotting oars, and several inconspicuous holes, sitting with quiet contempt as we slowly sink.

Near the very end, as Mr. Denis is on his way out, Karri walks back in, having returned from eating lunch. I'm not entirely sure how, but eventually the subject of dogs comes up, and Karri (a tremendously gifted artist) mentions that she's sketching Savo's pugs for him. I should point out that Mr. Savo has an all-out obsession with his pet pugs. So much so that he periodically waves to the pictures of them that sit on the desk in his office. For the artistic occasion, he has taken several more pictures of them for Karri to sketch. Foulds inquires as to whether or not she can draw his beagles as well. She answers that she can, as soon as she's finished with Savo's pugs.

You can all see the direction this is going in, right? Right, so Foulds grabs the pictures of the pugs neatly sitting on Savo's bookshelf, and runs out of the room. Kate, Karri, and myself are stunned by this stunt. We yell out to him, "Savo's going to kill you!" Foulds cackles madly, foolishly thinking that he's going to get away with it. My thoughts contain no doubts about his fate: He is a dead man.

The bell now rings for the end of the second lunch wave and the beginning of the third. Kate bids us a farewell that she tries to drag out as long as possible. She sighs heavily as I reassure her with, "Breathe deep, Kate. Breathe deep and endure" — the same advice that I've always given. She's not thrilled with the idea of having to go back to geometry, and I don't blame her. I remember having geometry class, and I remember it being one of the most hellish episodes of my life. As it is now, I'm still not looking forward to advanced algebra next period. But please, let us not speak of such things now. Just enjoy the moment while we still have it.

Savo walks back in, and Karri and I stare at him, pausing for his reaction. We sit wide-eyed with empty visages, like little kids waiting for fireworks to explode. Savo knows something is up, and instinctively looks to where his pug pictures once stood. He goes from being horrified, to sad, to angry in a matter of just a few seconds, and then turns to us for answers. He seems strangely calm about this whole thing. "Would either of you two know where the pictures of my pugs have gone to?"

Karri looks at me with a sly grin, carefully picking her words in order to milk the most delectation out of what is happening. "I don't know where those pug pictures are. Do you know where they are, Stefan?" Her coy tone is begging me to play along.

"No, Karri. I don't have the slightest clue as to where they might be."

We might be thoroughly relishing this, but Savo is clearly very distressed. "Well, they just didn't get up and walk out on their own, did they? Is it possible that someone might have taken them?"

Karri isn't about to give in that easily, and she'd be most displeased if I did. "There might have been someone in here," she answers.

"Yes, I think I recall somebody coming in here. I can't quite remember—my memory isn't what it used to be," I add. That's no lie, it really isn't. My long-term has trouble remembering anything past eighth grade, and my short-term is completely shot.

After dropping a few ambiguous hints here and there, Savo asks in earnest, "Could they be with Foulds?" Well, hot damn—give this man a prize! We at last relate to him that Foulds has stolen the pictures, and reveal his motive for doing so. He heaves a deep sigh, almost as if he regrets what must be done next. Pulling out his top desk drawer, he hunts around in the unwonted junk that has been collecting there over the years. He ultimately finds what he was searching for—a steak knife, probably five or six inches in length, its metallic shine gleaming in the florescent light of the office. Brandishing it with great dexterity, and checking the blade to make sure it is still sharp, he asks me, "I dunno, do you think this could cut an artery?"

I then share with him a little bit of advice that I habitually give to anyone who comes to me seeking violence recommendations. "Either through the heart, the throat, or in through the ear to the brain. Those are the weak points." With that, he saunters out, seemingly set on his task.

Karri gives me the "What the hell does he think he's doing, and what the hell are you telling him *that* for?" look.

I give her the "What the hell were you expecting?" look. Both of us are silent for about five minutes. Actually, I'm a bit surprised; I thought he was going to go for the letter opener or the box cutter, or even the golf club that's sitting in the corner.

How to Deal with Spare Time

It is not worth an intelligent man's time to be in the majority. By definition, there are already enough people to do that.
—G. H. Hardy

Working in the Guidance Department, and I use the word "working" very loosely, has taught me how to cope with spare time. It's a bit of an odd statement, because anyone who has lived in the real world (and I mean the *real* real world, not that bullshit *Real World* on MTV) for more than ten minutes knows that if you have spare time, then it is a short-lived experience. And if, for some peculiar reason, you hold on to that spare time, people will find you and inform you that you are wasting your life. I know this because I've had spare time on several occasions, and people just start coming out of the woodworks. In Guidance, spare time is not something that you have while you're not working—it is the work. Savo regularly says to me whilst exiting the office, "Alright, take any phone calls, man the fort, lock up when you leave," etcetera, etcetera. So I sit there—in his chair, if I so choose—waiting for something to happen. I've spent many a day waiting for something. It's like being the night watchman of a city that's not worth attacking in the first place.

Being in Guidance has also given me plenty of spare time to meet the alternative crowd. You know, the kind of people that the system would lock up in a small, dark, secluded room if they had the option. (Sometimes they do—it's called in-school suspension.) To be honest, I think we should keep more of these people around, because they are the greatest self-esteem boosters one could ever ask for. I wouldn't say that their standards are low; I just think that they are being realistic. When they walk in, the vast majority first want to know if they're passing. As soon as they find out that they are (if they are), they immediately want to know if they can drop a class. Now how's that for an odd brand of optimism? You've got to admire their enthusiasm for slacking, because I've never seen that line of thinking anywhere else but here.

And who, you ask, would be the best example of this? Why, that would be Heather, another senior whom I've had the pleasure of getting to know very well. She is the one who has (at least in my mind) taken slacking from being a popular pastime to a postmodern art form.

Speak of the devil. "Hi, Stefan!" Heather exclaims from the doorway of Savo's office. Her voice is overly enraptured, but not a single word of her jubilant speech is ever feigned or forced. She ambles in and makes herself at home; throws a pile of books and folders stuffed with old homework onto a nearby table, lays back in the chair closest to the door, puts her feet up on Savo's chair. Her attire is comprised of all her usual clothes—a grayish-white sweatshirt, sweatpants, white socks paired with Adidas sandals. Her blonde hair is pulled back into a ponytail, giving her an excuse not to do her hair in the morning. Her bangs hang down and fall just short of her lurid azure eyes, which are often half-closed while she rambles on agilely, but flare up whenever she's excited about something. She talks without direction or objective, changing subjects at random.

"Ugh..." she grumbles, "I have so much makeup work to do." After seeing all the time that she's taken off from school, I can't say that honestly surprises me. Remember, this is the same girl who showed up for school ten minutes late on a day when we already had a ninety-minute snow delay.

"I know. Shouldn't you start working on some of that?"

"I need my Stefan time!" she snaps. This is a relatively new development; it seems that there are several seniors who have found my verbose invectives to be an aphrodisiac for workday stress. "Why?" she asks, in a tone that manages to be both mocking and dead serious at the same time, "are you trying to get rid of me?!" Her eyes sparkle in their entire cerulean splendor.

I respond calmly and coolly, qualities that I've been trying to hone to perfection. "No, I'm just looking out for you."

"Awww, that's sweet..." she demurely answers. "Wait," she adds, the inquisitional tone returning, "are you being sarcastic?"

"No," I respond, doing my best to sound straightforward and candid.

Her voice lightens again into a gentle undertone. "Awww...thanks, Stefan." Heather has been having a lot of problems with academics, but it's nothing new. Her school records (which she dug out one day for kicks) reveal that she's been dealing with Attention Deficit Disorder since elementary, many of her teachers snidely remarking in scribbled writing at the bottom of the reports, "Heather socializes too much with the other students and has trouble staying in her seat." She laughed callously at their comments, and passed the papers around for everyone present to see, letting us share in her apparent victory over the system.

Her grades have been slipping all year, but she seems confident that she'll emerge from it all perfectly fine. I am not so sure, and bet her five bucks that she wasn't going to graduate this year. "Five bucks? You're on!...And you better pay me when I win!"

In my mind, it's the easiest five bucks I ever made. After that, she probably will graduate, if only just to ridicule me. She has even stuck with her senior math class, which I had thought to be a lost cause and had advised her to drop.

Heather is one of those types that inspire self-retrospection. Troubles never fail to make their way into her life. She's often sick—too often. Doctors have determined that there's something wrong with her thyroid, but have yet to figure out what exactly. "I'm dying, Stefan," she emphatically states on the days when she struggles to walk from class to class. It's heartbreaking to see her on those days. Normally, she is instilled with so much passion, working toward every goal and ambition, even if from the start it seems impossible. That's more zeal than I've ever had. When she's in a good mood, unafraid to laugh and tell you stories about whatever comes to mind, talking with her is one of the best ways to spend spare time. "Well, I've gotta finish some projects," she says, after making some smalltalk. "I just wanted to say 'hi' to you because I haven't done that in awhile...Bye."

"Later, Heather," I reply solemnly, without a moment's hesitation.

One of the best ways that I've found to spend spare time is to sleep. You've got to be careful, though, because although just about everybody complains about being tired, no one will so much as think twice before poking fun if they catch you sleeping—the occasional kid stepping in to ask, "Hey, man, havin' fun?" and then me quietly responding with, "Loads of it...jackass." I usually keep a quiver full of parting shots in case of an emergency. The logic behind anti-sleep sentiments has eluded me thus far. Perhaps it is true that we're not a people of action, but rather a people of endless bitching. I speak from personal experience when I say that bitching is more fun than action. Laziness takes precedence over action merely because action would require a certain degree of movement.

If, by chance, you were to look at our schedule arrangements, you might get a grasp on why we we're so lethargic. During first period, we're too tired to do anything. During second period, we are still too tired to do anything. By third period, we're pretty awake and able to understand what's going on. Once fourth period rolls around, we're all anticipating lunch, and are too hungry and solicitous to handle anything. While in fifth and sixth, we have just eaten lunch and hit a sudden low. When we finally arrive at seventh, we're all excited about going home and can't focus on any kind of material, no matter how basic in nature. That's essentially our day, in a nutshell. One class per day, forty-five minutes of learning. And now we're even giving up on that. Or maybe that's just me.

The third lunch is the quietest of the four, with few people passing in or out. This is the time that, if I had any athletic director-type work to do, I would do it. There's a lot of leeway given to me on most projects. I'm allowed to work at my own leisure, and at whatever pace I choose. Thinking about this job makes me think about how much harder everything used to be. I remember the teachers in elementary school trying to scare us by telling us tales of the horrors and difficulties of high school. What they failed to mention was that none of the horrors or the difficulties were academically related.

If I really stretch my memory, which is not easy to do considering all of the elasticity that it's lost over the years, I would name sixth grade as being the most oppressive and demanding of all of my years of schooling. Those were the days of endless projects— up to six at a time—that were all due during the same week. It was the closest I've ever been to going insane. Those were the days when my grade was based more on using pretty colors than on content. Bullshit if you're telling me that was supposed to prepare me for high school. Nothing could have prepared me for high school—not all the D.A.R.E. programs, motivation assemblies, and best-of-luck speeches in the world. And I did have one of those best-of-luck speeches at my eighth-grade graduation ceremony. I still can't believe that we actually had an eighth-grade graduation ceremony.

The fourth lunch wave is the hot spot, or was, in any event. Fourth lunch was when the regular crew of seniors came into guidance during my freshman year. The senior room filled up way too fast, and since they sure as hell weren't going to go to the cafeteria, Savo's office served as a kind of refugee camp for them. This was the time that I was taught every vile truth about high school that there was to know. Most of them must've felt that I was a kind of ambassador to the freshman class, because they brought their complaints about them to me regularly. "I hate your class soooo much! No offense…"

"That's alright," I told them, "I do, too." At first, they were surprised when they found out that I was a freshman, saying, "You don't act like one." That, I must confess, is the highest-paid compliment that I've received to date. My ultimate goal had been achieved: to mature beyond my years, and to shake off this old stigma that I'm too young to do or be able to understand anything. Getting to that point was a lengthy expedition, and it was a hard-won victory.

The seniors during my freshman and sophomore years in high school were among those who were the best influence on me. I met every shade of eccentric in all degrees, and each one had something to offer—if not advice, then at least a laugh or two. If you are someone who is about to go into high school, remember that seniors can be the greatest source of wisdom as to how to get through it. To get through, you might say, life itself (though they can also be the greatest source of irritation at times, as well). There were several little pieces of information that they all agreed upon:

- Being a freshman sucks.
- Jobs and work suck.
- People suck.
- Classes (most of them) suck.
- A few even branched out to inform me: Prom sucks.
- And this was the bonus for the next generation: high school sucks.

Yes, they were a people of few, yet precise, words. When you're a freshman, you naturally assume that shit happens to you because you are who you are in terms of age. By the time you're a senior, you seem to become much more philosophical about the situation. They can see why things are going wrong. It's like the train wreck in slow motion theorem.

It seems that tension really starts to build up during the senior year. The need to get into college, to do well on the SATs, to get a job (or having to deal with work), to pass these last few classes, the strain of keeping relationships together, to have to deal with the drama and gossip that surrounds prom—they all start to escalate and magnify each other exponentially. Every day is another story of trying to deal with a group of people who they've all learned to hate. It tends to get under your skin. I've seen people break down right in front of me, the pressures having finally brought them to the threshold of what they are able to withstand. They've given me the best advice of my life as to how to deal when everything is closing in on you, when things are about to go from dark to pitch-black.

But maybe the saddest fact of reality that I am often forced to face is that it was all so very short-lived. What I'm left with are mostly memories. Sometimes, it feels like all I've got are memories. Vague recollections of every time that was happier than now. I'm still trying to tell myself that that's not true, but with not much success. I think that's the best way to spend spare time. Sitting quietly in the corner of the room, fading in and out, watching the clock slowly burn off the remaining time. Trying to think about everything that's happened today, everything that happened yesterday, and not bothering to care about what's going to happen tomorrow.

So, as I sit here contemplating my short, ineffectual life, quietly laughing to myself as I imagine what would happen if that antique desk were to burst into flames, I hear the bell ring. It's time to leave. It's time to continue this downward spiral into oblivion elsewhere. There never was any point in wasting time getting to the inescapable.

Miscellaneous Philosophy—Part 6
I'm Not Required to Care

I was on About.com's Teen Advice section and saw an article entitled "10 Things You Oughta Know About Stealing." And I thought, "This is going to be good."

Every time that I start to get happy, I think about reality.
Then I stop smiling.

The Irish have St. Patrick's Day, and what better way to celebrate a saint's day than to go out and get drunk? There are all sorts of ethnicities with their own special spin: The Irish get to drink a lot, Italians get to eat pasta and work in the "family business," and the Jews get to be, well, Jewish. I'm Finnish—what do I get? That's what I always hated about these ethnic days. When you see an Irish guy inebriated on St. Patrick's Day, all is well in the world. When you see a Finnish guy wasted, it's just sad.

There are three things that I can't do: fake sincerity and math.

An Italian mafia is predictable. Now a Finnish mafia...no one would expect that! A bunch of tall Scandinavians suddenly show up outside your front door one night, "Ay, we'll beat ye' to death with fish, we will!"

When I come home from school on an average day, the first thing that I reach for is the Ibuprofen. The stuff works wonders. But then, you get a few of those really bad days where you have to step it up to something like Advil or Tylenol Extra Strength. You start getting use to that, and before you know it, nothing but

Midol will do. That's the problem right there: Ibuprofen is the gateway drug.

When taking an online quiz about whether or not you're ready to have sex, "Don't Care" is never the right answer.

Chapter Nine

No matter how much sleep, no matter how good of a day, no matter how energetic I was earlier, the afternoons always catch me off guard. You'd think that after so many years of both high school and middle school I'd be prepared, having seen it coming, but I'm not. All of a sudden, the whole thing hits you like a ton of bricks, and all you want to do is go home. The hallways are choked to their gagging points with all of the kids coming out of the cafeteria and up the stairs—the only set of stairs on this side of the school that go to the second floor. I have to go up there, and wouldn't you know it? It's like gridlock rush hour (only not funny in the way that Jackie Chan and Chris Tucker made it. Twice). The going is slow, and each step sucks the life right out of you. The damned thing feels like Everest, only there's no spectacular view at the top.

Worst of all, you don't even get the feeling of relief when you're finally done. Once you're there, you have to journey down more hallways to get to class. And you most certainly won't feel relieved when you reach your class. This is especially true with the class that I'm heading to now—that of advanced algebra. I hate, hate, hate, *hate math*!

Holy Sh*t...
I Just Realized How Much I Hate Math

"Math...math, my dear boy, is nothing more than the lesbian sister of biology."

—*Peter Griffin*, Family Guy

I used to be a good student in all of my subjects. When I started nearing the end of middle school, it quickly became apparent that that was going to have to change. All at once, there was more material in each and every class than had ever existed before, and for whatever reason, it became absolutely imperative that we learn all of it. Before, most of it was pretty manageable. Way back when (in eighth grade), I used to be the one who learned everything in class and then taught it to everyone else five minutes before school started. I was good at that. Believe it or not, I used to be considered smart…used to be.

But times change, and there's usually nothing you can do about it. I decided that one of my subjects was going to have to be sacrificed for the greater good of the other four. Math instantly found itself at the top of the hit list. It was an excellent candidate for liquidation, considering that I had been slipping in it ever since the teacher started putting letters into the equations. To me, that crosses a line in the sand that, in terms of logic, should not be crossed. Once that happened, I told myself, "Y'know, self, this math stuff doesn't really seem to be all that it's cracked up to be." And then memory chimes in, "Yes, I concur."

It's weird, too, because I tend to stick to math for the first half of the year or so, and then I give up. For my part, I'm at least trying to look like I'm trying. As I waltz into advanced algebra (or on other days, tango, or maybe skedaddle, depending on my mood), the thought that comes across my mind every time that I walk in here comes up once again. That thought is: "How did I wind up like this?" It's a good question. What, at what point in time, caused me to be stuck in a place where I have to lie, cheat, and steal just to subsist? Every day, I'm treading on a thin line between brilliant scheme and total disaster. Every day, I think that this will be the day—the day that they finally come to their senses and reach the objective of proving that I don't have the slightest clue as to what I'm doing. Every day, I think that they'll catch me, and that every borrowed piece of homework and calculator trick will come back to bite me in the ass. It hasn't happened yet, but someday, I swear …

It's hard to describe where I sit in here because the seats were changed on a fairly regular basis. But my all-time favorite is where I'm at now—in the very back corner of the room, completely detached from the rest of the class. It's an orange reclining desk, named as such for the attached seat that's been purposely bent backward to allow for maximum comfort. You can achieve some record-breaking slouching in one of these things. Sometimes, I maneuver it behind a large filing cabinet so that I can take a breather from the numerical workout. I could even bring in magnets to post cheat sheets (convenience sheets) on it. Never had the need to, but it's nice to know that I've got the option of doing so.

Seated directly to my left is Neil. Neil is the Indian (as in of India, not Native American) in our school. I mention it only because the Indian minority in the entire student body is approximately three people. I say "approximately" because there are always a few kids with questionable backgrounds. I also mention it because, at times, it seems as if this teacher of ours has something against white kids (or sympathy for Indians). And unlike some of my other claims, I have some proof to back this one up.

There was a certain homework assignment that the two of us had participated in a cooperative learning experience in order to complete. We both had the exact same answers and the exact same work—the only thing that was different was the names on the paper. I received a ninety, but Neil got a perfect hundred! Outrageous? You bet your ass it was! Another instance of injustice was a paper on which we both used calculators to complete the work. I got a sixty on it for that old arch nemesis (yes, I have a lot of those) of a phrase, "No Work, No Credit." What bullshit. He got a hundred on it simply because he wrote, "All Work Done On Calculator" on the side of the paper. I didn't know we could do that! Well, I learned my lesson. From then on, that little phrase appeared on every math paper I handed in. It became a standard inscription, right along with the name and date in the upper-right hand corner.

Don't worry; the teacher finally caught on to that scurvy knave, Neil. When he took a test that he didn't know the solutions for, he wrote, "Look on the answer key. I assure you that the answer is there." That didn't cut it. Although I must admit, it was a valiant effort on his part, and it was unquestionably better than my fake answer of writing "N/A" on the blank of every query that

I didn't comprehend. It's been a while since I've had any passing grades in here.

Math classes haven't been my strong point since eighth grade. That's where it started going downhill. I could never quite understand slope. Sure, I get the basic concept of it, but if I were to give you the equation $x = 2y2 + 5$, would you be able to graph that? Well, in any case, I wouldn't. I've told some of my fellow classmates in times past that I didn't understand slope, and they all have the same reaction. They first put on the best horror/awe expression that I've ever seen (and each one gets better each time), and they immediately shout the following phrase at me: "Rise over run!" Dammit to hell! I don't know what that means! Stop yelling! It's been a long journey from there.

Algebra, Latin, and Incest: Three Things That You'll Never Need to Succeed in Life

If you have always done it that way, it is probably wrong.
—Charles Kettering

There are so many math concepts that seem so highly unnecessary; it's hard to know where to start. For example: Things in this world got a little crazier the day that I walked into advanced algebra and the teacher said, "Today, we'll be going over imaginary numbers." What exactly are imaginary numbers, you ask? Why, imaginary numbers are numbers that don't exist. So just picture being taught an entire lesson about numbers that don't exist, how to write equations with numbers that don't exist, and best of all, determining the solutions to equations with numbers that don't exist. Do you know what the answer is to an equation with imaginary numbers? It doesn't matter, because they're *fucking* imaginary! How can you have an equation that results in an imaginary number? Didn't we used to call that a *wrong* equation?

How does one get an imaginary number? Well, my friends, imaginary numbers are the direct result of doing something stupid. Really *stupid*. Most of the time, you get them by taking the square root of a negative number. To think that someone, at some point in his life, spent time making something like this up is just disturbing. If your idea of enjoying yourself on the weekend is to sit around making up fake numbers, you need to seek professional help immediately. What's even worse is that other people, for centuries on end, believed him. Why wasn't there somebody who stopped and said, "Imaginary numbers? Jim, you're pretty fucked up. You need to get a girlfriend, seriously, dude. This has gone way too far." It's weird, isn't it? People who have imaginary friends are locked up, but people who can come up with theorems for imaginary numbers are considered geniuses.

In crazy-man's math, we also have rational numbers and irrational numbers. Rational numbers are your normal, average, all-around good numbers. Not taken to either extreme, they'll act appropriately in most equations. Then you have your irrational numbers, which are numerics *on the edge*. They're unpredictable, and don't behave conventionally in any situation. They'll take your numerator of a fraction and transform into some kind of twisted, odious "x square root of 7" deals. They're a bad influence on all the numbers around them. They were probably good numbers at one point or another, but I guess they kinda fell into the wrong crowd. Y'know, the old drinking, drugs, and reciprocal overdoses. They don't make any sense, but instead of saying, "They don't make any sense, the equation must be wrong," we just make up a different name for them.

You can almost picture the mathematician who made up that one to save his ass from looking stupid in front of all this computational buddies at the annual Nobel Prize winners meeting. "So, 'y' plus or minus the square root of 3x2 equals ð7 (ø)."

All the others look at his ghastly scribbled excuse for mankind's thinking process on paper. "Hey Bill, if you factor out x and divide both sides of the quadratic by ð...you get a different result. Bill, your equation is wrong."

Bill panics and quickly comes up with something that makes him look smart. "No, it's not! The result is simply...different. That makes it an 'irrational' number. Yes, that'll work. It's just an irrational equation!"

The dignitaries nod in approval. "Ah, yes; I see it now! Of course, it is an 'irrational' number!"

Several hundred years later, we're tolerating the humiliating upshot of one man's imagination gone amiss and his pride inflating to twice its normal size, like some kind of weird Amazonian lizard defending itself from predators.

How do we manage to survive all the insanity? We rely on our machines to carry us up and above the floodwaters of lunacy. For thousands of years, it was the abacus that guided us through the onslaught of extraneous concepts. Then, it was something that the elders call a "slide-rule." I have no idea what that is, so don't ask me. Then came the calculator, basic at first, but then adapting to the growing needs of the average stupid kid. Today, we have the TI-83 Texas Instruments graphing calculator, the behemoth of all calculation machines. It just goes to show you that everything really *is* big in Texas. Each one has fifty buttons, each of which has two or three different roles. Sometimes I think that it has more program options than there are arithmetic operations. Most math teachers don't even know what all of the implementations are for.

There are some intriguing keys on that device. I was first attracted to the "MATRX" key. Much to my disappointment, it does not temporarily suspend the laws of physics. Why don't you crush *another* dream while you're at it, math class? There's also a "sin" key, which will not scroll redemption across the screen as I had hoped. There's a "tan" key, but no matter how many times you hit it, it won't give you one. I got all excited when I saw the "MATH" key, because I figured, "Now I don't even need to learn all of this stuff! I can just hit the MATH button and it will do all the sweat and toil applications for me!" Alas, it does not work like that. There just so happens to be a "MODE" key, but sadly, there is no way to set it to "REALITY." Because of their vast quantity, you'll never, ever, ever use all of the calculator capabilities. And if you do, you have no life and need to give up now. Take it from me, folks, I've lived life once or twice before.

That will all work out pretty well, right up until the point that you get a ditto that can't be solved with calculator alone. I saw a word problem on one particular ditto that diagrammed a person standing near a building and another person on top of the building, looking down at the other person standing near the building. It was being used as an example of how to use sine, cosine, and tangent to find the angles of a triangle, but that's not what you saw. What you saw was a man on a building, angles of depression, and a man at the point of a triangle. In other words, what you saw was a diagram of the Kennedy assassination. Would I lie about something like that? All this time we've been blaming kids for bringing violence into schools, but now we have proof that schools are bringing violence into kids. Any student could see that and say, "Oh, that's how you're supposed to measure that angle? It's a good thing you told me. Otherwise, I might have missed."

Soon after we received that ditto and had brought up its striking resemblance to the Kennedy assassination, Neil related to me that he had a dream about this math problem. In it, he was an FBI agent who was protecting Kennedy when the motorcade went through Houston. After the former President was shot, Neil fired randomly at the rooftop where the bullet was discharged (as is standard FBI-agent procedure). When he went to the top of the building, he found the body of the killer. Imprinted on his hand was the acronym for remembering the sine (opposite over hypotenuse), cosine (adjacent over hypotenuse), and tangent (opposite over adjacent) functions: SohCahToa...*I am SO scared.*

If you were to come into the classroom during the middle of one of these simply enthralling math lessons, you'd notice that almost all of us have the same contortion upon our faces. We're all staring blankly at the board, watching it fill up with numbers. We gape at it like something sooner or later is going to happen, and we don't want to miss it for the world. Maybe, right when it's time to leave, an enchanted leprechaun will jump out and holler, *"Surprise!"* Then a little light bulb will click on in our heads and it will all make sense. Like magic. Or maybe the teacher will write "S =" and a stream of Skittles will burst out right there in front of us. Then the enchanted leprechaun will tell us—in the thickest Irish accent imaginable—"Top o' the mornin' to ya! Might ye want to have a little taste of the rainbow? It's magically delicious!" Well, a man can dream, can't he?

But they were all the aspirations of an old fool. For once I cared to snap back to reality, a place that I do visit on occasion, all the illusions fade away, and I remember that there is no rainbow, no leprechaun, and no Skittles (although I'm more of a Starburst man myself). Just an overflow of numbers and worthless knowledge. And let's make it clear to everyone that the stuff is worthless. There's no need to humor ourselves by trying to dupe everyone into thinking that we'll use it at some point. The only way that you would need any of this is if you're planning on becoming a math teacher. That is to say, if you plan on infecting and inflicting future generations of hapless boys and girls with this garbage, the lot of them forced to swallow the awful arithmetical refuse because a state law mandates it. Buddha help us all.

You can't possibly tell me that I'm going to have to factor a polynomial in order to pay my taxes. I sure as hell hope not, because I don't know how to factor polynomials. First of all, I don't know what a "polynomial" is exactly. I know "poly" is Greek for "multiple," and I know that "nomial" is…also Greek, but that's about it. Secondly, even if I knew what a polynomial was, I don't know what the word "factor" implies. Solve? Rearrange? Make simple? I may or may not have been in school the day that we started going over them, but if I was, I have no recollection of it. As soon as the teacher said, "Today, we'll be going over how to factor polynomials," my brain instantaneously went into a power-save mode, and shut down to conserve energy for more useful functions (like breathing).

That was the last line I heard. I awoke ten or fifteen minutes later, just in time to hear, "…and that's the most important thing that you'll need to remember for the test." Crap. The quiz later that week resulted in a thirty-eight for a grade. Laughing, to me, seemed like the most logical response. So I did. The teacher got in front of the room and said, "Some of these grades were good, some of them were…well, what do you think would be a good word to use, Stefan?"

"Well, the word 'abhorrent' comes to mind," I said jokingly. Looking at it, I noticed that, after completing number one (with the wrong answer), I had lost thirty-six points. In other words, I had already failed the quiz by the time I had answered the first question. C'mon! That's not even fair! *Life's not fair, Stefan.* Shuddup, voice of reason!

I'm not sure if I cared about it that much. Some kids worry about grades to no end. I worry about grades to a point—that point at which something requires effort. I don't mind putting effort into things that are worthwhile, but grades are not something that fit my definition of "worthwhile." I always felt that getting good grades was like investing in the stock market. It's something that you don't have any control over. You just have to know when to buy and when to sell, and likewise, when to try and when to give up and go home. And sitting in this class at the moment, there's nothing that I would like to do better than to go home.

Not surprisingly, I've never held myself accountable for my poor behavior. That would only lower my self-esteem, and perish the thought that we do that. The easiest target would be the teacher. Surely, we would have been able to construe within our thoughts the method behind the madness if only we had a better teacher? I doubt that more and more nowadays. I'm pretty sure that math would be this messed up no matter who was teaching it. Our teacher was another one of those types that could randomly go off on tangents. She once started talking to one of her students about a golf tournament that he was in while discussing a math problem in mid-sentence. That takes either a whole lot of skill, or a whole little of an attention span. In another episode, she started explaining how her husband became successful by getting his Bachelor of Science degree. That led to one of my most beloved lines yet, that she herself spoke: "You can do anything you want in life as long as you've got the BS to go with it." How very true. *Sniff* I will cherish that forever.

When time comes to do the homework, which we often have a chance to do in class, the time also comes for me to find somebody who can help make sense of all these complicated computation questions. Bob always helps out a lot. For those of you not in the know, "Bob" is an acronym for "back of book," where the answers to all the odd-numbered questions are. We have to come up with a new code word, though. I think some of the teachers are starting to catch on.

Neil couldn't do much math, but there was one thing that he was good at: programs. He could configure programs into our TI-83 graphing calculators (then standard issue), which could do most of the work for us. Neil was also the one who gave us all blackjack. He downloaded the program and gave it to the lot of us. That game is the work of the devil, I swear. For two weeks, I couldn't stop playing it! And you always lose because the dealer cheats! I don't know much about blackjack, but I do know that the dealer is supposed to stay at sixteen. But he never does! He *always* hits, and he *always* gets a five, and nails the blackjack! Bastard. I lost over a quarter of a million dollars in less than half an hour. We're still waiting for Duck Hunt to be distributed to the masses.

Yes, Neil was always kind to us when it came to programming our calculators. Except for that one time when he screwed up the formula and accidentally graphed our equations on our blackjack tables. There was a lot of racial slurring going on that day. Which is unusual, considering that Neil is originally from New Jersey. I always win the race arguments between the two of us. I have some background information on Hinduism and Indian culture that I taught myself during my world history class last year (since it wasn't part of the regular curriculum). I can come up with some real conversational gems, like, "Hey, how's Vishnu doin'?" or "So, any thoughts about what animal you're going to be reincarnated as?"

He tries to fight back, but there aren't a lot of Finnish stereotypes to work with. The best he can do is, "Shouldn't you be out catching fish somewhere?" and "It's pretty cold out today, but I guess you're use to it, right?" It's not that I'm a racist; it's just that I think that race is too fun of a subject to openly ignore.

In all likelihood, if you wanted really good, accurate answers, you went to Sean. Sean was, is, and forever will be a thousand times smarter than our entire class's intelligence combined. He could look at a polynomial, configure the equation, and figure out the answer in the same amount of time that it took me to just copy the answer from Bob. *Son of a bitch, that's smart!* As you might expect, he was not very popular among the populace because of his intellect. It stemmed from the fact that, no matter how hard you tried, your work always looked like shit by comparison.

His antics aren't anything like the performance that Mikey will put on when he does math. And if you've ever seen Mikey do math, you'd understand what I'm talking about. I had a study hall with him during my freshman year, and to this day, I must avow that I've never seen anything quite like it. He stares at the paper, pencil in hand, deeply contemplating the problem to the best of his contemplating abilities. He then starts listing random numbers in a spot-on Sean Connery impersonation. After itemizing six or seven numbers, he'll lift his hands to the sky and wait for the answer to come to him. Sure enough, after a slight pause, it does. He writes it down, and repeats the process for the next one. I don't know if it is coincidental osmosis, divine intervention, or if it is just a random bit of jackassary, but it works.

By the way, "jackassary" is a real word. Webster's dictionary defines it as "the quality or state of being a jackass." Look it up some time. I think you'd be surprised to find that I'm not all pomp and circumstance...whatever that means.

What it comes down to is a big waste of time. When you first sit down, the massive white board in the front of the room is almost entirely blank. Then, the teacher starts talking. You'll lose her train of thought after a few sentences. If not, then at least by the time she uses one of those really big words, like "polynomial," or "equation," or "congruent." In any case, while she's talking, the board will start filling up with numbers and equations. No one, absolutely no one (except for maybe Sean), knows what's going on. Numbers are appearing, the teacher is talking, and nothing has so much as the slightest bit of significance. Even if you knew what was happening, you'd soon be slumbering peacefully from trying to pay attention. Every so often you'd be able to pick up a line or two, but taken out of context, they don't make any sense. Hell, when they were *in context* they didn't make any sense. You might hear something like, "Do you want to take the cube root then square it or do you want to take the square root and then cube it?" Who gives a rat's ass? It's not like one of them is easier. Not that I can remember which one is easier. It's math, and that means it's difficult.

Or maybe you'll get something that comes after a long line of lecture, and be asked, "What do you do if the coefficient is a negative number?" The same thing that I do when the whatchamacallit is a positive number—ask Sean what the answer is. Surely he will know. And if he doesn't, then it either doesn't have an answer or wasn't worth figuring out in the first place.

All jesting aside, there is a general pattern to the teachings. At the beginning of any given chapter, there will be a lengthy and taxing explanation of some impossible numerical theory that cannot possibly be used for anything. We will then spend upward of a week struggling in vain to decipher its meanings and make out how we're going to use it on the next test. Then, at the very end of the chapter, it will be revealed, to the bewilderment of us all, that all along there was a remarkably easy calculator key sequence that could do all the hard work for you. "Why didn't you tell us this before?!" asks the class in a state of frenzy, humiliated at the indignity of it all.

The teacher proceeds to come up with some bullshit along the lines of, "You need to know how to do this without the calculator! What would you do if, on the day of the test, the batteries in all the calculators simultaneously died?"

I'm not taking that as an excuse! By this point, as I'm nearly in a state of madness, I shout out, "Now what are the collective odds of that happening?!" Mikey joins in from across the room, "Pretty slim, dammit!" After a while, I started to think, "Y'know, why try? After all, trying is the first step toward failure." Everyone always gets a kick out of that.

The class carries on for many a minute, each of which feels like an hour, and each of which drains the very essence of life from us. We apprehensively monitor the clock, damning time for not passing fast enough. Every class is like that. Each period, we count down the minutes until it's over, and then celebrate when it at last arrives at its termination, only to do the whole thing over again in the next one. We don't care. Over and over again, counting down the minutes, hours, days, weeks, months; living from vacation to vacation. Sounds pretty pathetic, doesn't it? We've been doing it for ten years now. Nonetheless, we watch the clock with the greatest of anticipation, silently shouting at the minute hand to "Move faster, dammit!" We hope, we pray, we become more religious then we've been all day. In a crisis condition such as this, I can't help but quietly laugh to myself as I wonder what it would be like if the light fixtures were to suddenly burst into flames.

RIIIIIIIIIINNNNNNNGGGGGGGGGGGGG!!!

Finally! Took ye' long enough! We can at last leave this place and begin the long journey ho—wait, there's another class?! Son of a bitch! We're not done yet! There's another class! *Fuck!*

Miscellaneous Philosophy — Part 7
Yes, You Can Quote Me on That

Do you know what's great about being a pessimist? At best, you're pleasantly surprised, and at worst, everything turns out exactly how you expected it to in the first place.

I've met a few people who act kind of crazy and tell me that they're "high on life." That was all well and good up until the point that I found out that "life" was the new street term for crack cocaine.

It's not that I lie, it's just that I bend the truth…into a pretzel.

Disney is one of the most insane organizations that humanity has to deal with in the modern age. If you need some proof, look no further than the movie *Holes*, an adaptation of a book of the same name by Louis Sachar. A movie review of *Holes* said that it was "Good wholesome Disney fun!" Disney themselves said that it was "Fun for the whole family!" I have read this book, and for those of you not familiar with it, the majority of its contents consist of descriptions of young boys who are being held in a juvenile detention slave camp in the middle of a desert. Their punishment? To dig a hole as deep and as wide as their shovel every day. And if they die in the process, their name is simply crossed off from the list. It's a kind of twisted view on the American-justice-system-meets-Auschwitz. Now let me ask you this: If this is what Disney considers good and wholesome fun for the whole family, then
What the fuck is wrong with Disney?!

Just once, I'd like to listen to a rap ballad remix in which the artist does not mention the fact that it's a remix within the song itself. Just once.

Ambition is a bitch. It takes you in all the wrong directions.

I read a quote by Mark Twain that said, "There is nothing sadder than a young pessimist." And I thought, "Fuck you, Twain."

Chapter Ten

Okay, no worries. I'll just take a few deep breaths and endure this one last class. I've gotten this far—surely I can handle one more. Oh, but wouldn't you know? I have Spanish now. Not only is the class boring and tedious, but it's boring and tedious *in another language.*

I trudge down this one last hallway, to go to this one last class, to endure this one last crucible. The work in Spanish class probably wouldn't be that difficult if the instructions weren't also in Spanish. Then, if you do or say something incorrectly, the teacher (a native-born Sardinian, fluent in both Spanish and Italian) yells at you in Spanish, and you don't have the slightest clue as to what you are doing wrong. This class is our third year of Spanish, so everything about it is Hispanic, and your grade drops for every word of English you say. If you don't know what you're doing, you're screwed. But I guess you could say that about any class.

¡Hola! ¿Como estás? (Hi! How are you?)

I personally think we developed language because of our deep inner need to complain.

—Jane Wagner

I have a seat near the door, which I specifically picked at the beginning of the year with strategic elements in mind. Its location makes it great for quick exiting, as well as quick entrances. Always useful, because our teacher, Señora Pom, will make you sing if you're late. No one who has been late has sung in front of the class yet, opting to take the tardy instead; with the exception of Joe, who sang half of "I'm a Little Tea Pot" near the beginning of the year. (He got the first two lines down and forgot the rest.) Everyone has been begging me to purposely be late so I can sing them a song of the piano man, but I haven't given in to the peer pressure thus far. It's a shame, too, because one should always give in to peer pressure.

Señora Pom is, to put it bluntly, a short woman, her total height not being more than five feet. She was originally from Sardinia, which, at this point in time, is part of Italy. That's a good thing, because it is far too insignificant to be its own country. I told her that once, and immediately picked up on some bad vibes, some negative energy flowing between us, if you will. I often find it difficult to take her authority seriously, since the orders are being given to me by someone who is about a foot-and-a-half shorter than I am. I have to keep a good amount of distance between her and me while going down stairs, since I'm always afraid that I'll step on her. Still, she wields power like a mailman gone postal. Sure, there are reasons behind the rage, but the rage is still deemed highly uncalled for.

I'm one of the first ones to walk in, and as such I am a prime target for casual Spanish conversation. As Pom surveys the teaching arena, she opens up with, "¡Hola Estefan! ¿Como estás? (Hi Stefan! How are you?)" I get asked this a lot on a fairly regular basis (in English, of course). Everyone wants to know how you're doing, and I know the response, and it's been the same response for years. Things have been horrible. Things haven't been good in a long, *long* time. I've got homework, I've got projects, I've got grades to worry about, my parents are convinced that if I don't go to college and if I don't get a part-time job my life will be ruined, everyone's giving me advice that has to be followed to the word or else I'll regret it later, social relationships are caving in all around me, and *shit is happening*. But common courtesy dictates that I cannot say this. I have to smile, nod, and lie to the face of humanity that everything is *great* and that I'm having an *outstanding life*, each and every day. This theme is carried throughout all of my English conversations, and time and again, I feel obligated somehow to carry it over to Spanish. Where's the fun to be had in this? Where, I ask you? Where?

"Eh...masos o menos (More or less)."

Pom has been doing this teaching thing for a considerable amount of time, and by my tone of voice, she knows right away that something's up. She can also smell fear, I swear. "¿Porque su masos or menos? ¿Que estás esos? (Why are you 'more or less'? What's up?)"

The lot of us don't know much Spanish, despite this being our third year of it. But we do know a few key words and phrases that can get us through most dialogue. "Yo quisiera dormir (I want to sleep)."

"Ah, sí. Tú estás muy descansos, ¿verdad? (Ah, yes. You are very tired, right?)" Yeah, something like that. Soon after, the rest of the class shuffles in. An uneasy, nervous tension sets in that will last for the rest of our stay here. You know in the pit of your stomach that, at any moment, you could be called on to answer a question, with both question and answer in Spanish. You know that, at any moment, you could go from the smart-looking, high self-esteem, happy-go-lucky fellow to a dejected, melancholic, stupid piece of shit. Every breath is savored a little bit more than the last, because it may very well be your last. Happiness is fleeting.

Breathing heavy right with me is an interesting group of affiliates. Perhaps not quite as interesting as the history crowd, but to an extent, they are on that same level. Most of the characters you will all recognize from the start. To my left is Sean, the super-smart kid who will, upon a given signal, translate anything the teacher says. He has to. Otherwise, we won't have the faintest of ideas as to what's going on. To my right is Neil, the Indian kid from Jersey who's struggling through this class just as much as any. In front of Neil is Serena, who dreads Spanish just as much as she dreads history, and in front of Sean is Josh, the athletic, unearthly, Jolly Green Giant fellow from gym. But in front of me is someone I haven't yet fully discussed. You may remember him from my chapter on English class; you may remember him as that kid you saw in that place with those guys by the corner, but most of us remember him for that perfectly timed, well-spoken insult that just made us feel *pathetic*.

In front of me is Lucas—quick-witted, recalcitrant, conniving, magniloquent Luke. If you ever want to live your life feeling good about yourself, then you should probably avoid Luke. He can let out a line of rhetoric that can sink a battle cruiser, let alone your ego. Most people are either white or black, but Luke is a third color—orange (the word which he affluently pronounces with a New York accent). His hair is an orange beacon, cut with a short exactitude. His skin is imbued with an orange hue, and when it gets sunburned, it radiates a florescent tinge that almost glows in the dark. If you mess up in life in any way, shape, or form, and Luke is within earshot, he will verbally let you know of your shortcoming. This talent is especially deadly in Spanish, since we don't know Spanish. Believe me, he knows that we don't know Spanish. And we know that he knows that we don't know Spanish. And he knows that we know that he knows that we don't know Spanish. And so on.

I would never try to criticize Luke for his put-down comments or cutting remarks for any reason, however. He can be the nail in your coffin (assuming you dug the grave to begin with), but he can also be your saving grace, if he feels like it. A perfect example would be the end of a long day, not unlike this one, when I was simply pissed at the world. The class is going over vocabulary that no one has studied and no one knows—no one, except Neil. After correctly identifying the meaning of the tenth Spanish word in a row, I decide to extol Neil for his good studying habits. "Fuck you, Neil." Yes, I said it bluntly, truthfully, and—all things considered—a little too loudly.

Pom looks at me with a curious, yet still purely innocent look. "What did you say, Stefan?" Blame it on the tiring day; blame it on the racism of the moment, but for the first time in a long time, I am at a loss for words.

Enter Luke, impeccably poised directly in front of the teacher's line-of-sight, to keep me off the detention list. Without being asked or even so much as being prompted, he jumps in and answers, "He said, 'It was all *luck*, Neil.'" I thank him after class, but I'm pretty sure it wasn't gratitude that he was seeking. More like the feeling of helping those in need—a Mother Theresa for the slackers.

The very beginning of each class is very relaxing, as Pom plays some easy-going Spanish music and asks each of us how our day is going. This is intended to lure us into a false sense of security before she strikes. If you don't think she's going to strike, then your optimism has reached a point where it's eating itself for sustenance. Don't worry, though; Friday's quiz will smartly cure you of that. Spanish has several eccentricities that, from an English-speaking standpoint, don't make any sense. For those of you who have never attempted to learn Spanish, allow me to enlighten/warn/horrify you.

First and foremost, there are five different verb forms that vary depending on whether you're talking about yourself (yo), directly to someone else (tú), in the third person (el, ella, Ud.), ourselves (nosotros), or multiple other persons (ellos, ellas, Uds.). There is a sixth form (vosotros), but it is only used in a small area of Spain that you are never likely to be exposed to. Ever.

Besides this, there is an overabundance of verb tenses. There may only be three in English, but there are *eleven* in Spanish. And no, I am not shitting you. You have your standard-issue present, past, and future tenses. These are in conjunction with the indicative, meaning "definite," tense. Then there is a present subjunctive tense. You use subjunctive to imply something that is not definite, and subject to change. There is also an imperfect subjunctive (not to be confused with the imperfect tense), but to date, I don't know what that's used for. There's a present progressive, which has to do something with the word "estar" (to be). Don't ask me what, though. No lexicon would be complete without the potential tense, which, as the name infers, is used to describe something that may potentially happen. This may make it sound like the subjunctive tense, but they don't have anything in common whatsoever (except for being verb tenses). The perfect present, formal imperative, and the familiar imperative round out the vernacular Brady Bunch of linguistic little bastards. What I don't get is, when you're creating this language, and you're at ten verb forms...at what point do you look at all your Hispanic buddies and say, "Hey! Do you know what I think this language needs? *Another* verb tense! Yes! One hundred percent! Absolutely!"

All the verbs in the Spanish language have a slight change to them whenever you have a different tense or form. Most of them change in a relatively predictable way. Most of them. These are what you would call the "regular" verbs. Things can never be that simple, can they? Nope, they sure can't. Once you begin to understand the changes in regular verbs, you'll be introduced to the verbs that *don't* change in a relatively predictable way, known as the "irregular" verbs. Whenever one of these verbs changes tense or form, letters are added in and taken out at random. G's are put in haphazardly after L's; I's are changed to Y's; C's are substituted with Q's; and so forth. Once you understand both the regular and the irregular verbs, you'll be acquainted with the third variety of verbs that (if I may use a baseball analogy here) will throw you a curve ball—the "radical" verbs. Radical verbs take all the routine verb changes and say, "*Fuck you!*" They don't follow *any* rules, *any* patterns, and don't make *any* sense. If you don't believe me, look at the word "ir." The word "ir," under certain conditions, changes to the word "fui." Check and mate, rationality.

A widespread belief among the English-speaking peoples is that Spanish is loaded with cognates—that is, words that sound the same in both English and Spanish. Some even believe that all you need to do is add an "o" to the end of an English word to make it a Spanish word. Sometimes this is true, as in the word "rapido," which means (say it with me now) "rapid." For the grand majority of others words, however, this is not the case. Take the Spanish word "la tuna," por ejemplo (for example). I know what you're thinking, and you're wrong. The word "la tuna" is not Spanish for "the tuna." The word "la tuna" is Spanish for "the prickly pear." What is a prickly pear, you ask? From what I can gather, it is a type of fruit native to parts of Latin America, but don't hold me to that. The next time you're looking at a Spanish menu and you see tuna listed under the desserts, don't be surprised (or fooled).

Another favorite conundrum of mine is the Spanish word "la sopa." Doesn't it mean soap or soup? Soup or soap? If it means soap, then what's the word for soup? Conversely, if it's the word for soup, then what's the word for soap? If I'm in my luxurious five-star hotel in Madrid, and I call room service and ask them to bring me some sopa, do I really know what I'm getting? This would be an important thing to know, because I may end up washing with Campbells and eating the Dove exfoliater.

There is also an overabundance of terms in Spanish that tend to multitask. The Spanish word "el moza" means both "waiter" and "bellhop." If we go back to the luxurious five-star hotel in Madrid example (because I can afford things like that, being from Terryville and all), when I walk in and ask for the moza, I don't know whether I'm getting lunch or my bags brought to my room. What if the waiter isn't serving lunch yet? What if the bellhop is on break? What if I want the bellhop to bring me lunch? Then I'm really fucked.

What about those little accent marks? Contrary to popular belief, those things are not just for decoration. The slightest little feature can change the meaning of the word entirely. The word "este" has four different meanings just by where you place the accent mark. All the words in Spanish have four or five variant meanings, and most of the time you'll have no idea which one it implies. The word "que" can be used in a question to ask "What?" but in a regular statement, it can mean "than," "that," or "as." How can you tell which one is being utilized? Take your best guess.

When our whining reaches an unbearable level, Pom will teach us some Italian to lighten the mood. The Italian language makes the Spanish language look like a fun little code that we might have made up with our friends in our younger years. I won't go too in-depth with it, but I will point out this: The Italian language has almost three times as many articles as English. There's an entire different article form for masculine nouns that begin with the letter "Z." Again, I am not shitting you.

¡Yo no estoy de acuerdo! (I disagree!)

If hard work were such a wonderful thing, surely the rich would have kept it all to themselves.

—*Lane Kirkland*

There's always a lot of fascinating stuff going on in Spanish, and by "fascinating" I mean weird and unnecessarily perplexing. Spanish and English, the two language classes, are the two that have the most projects. In English, the undertakings are fun and creative, whereas in Spanish, they are drawn-out, pointless, and purposeless—the perfect way to end a perfectly bad day. An impeccable example would be the Spanish clothing flyer that I half-assed. It was more than a half-assed job. The best way I can phrase it is that I half-assed the half-assed. I quarter-assed the damn thing. A lot of effort was meant to be put into it, but at last second I decided that putting any effort into such a futile assignment would not only be unconscionable, but downright shameful. As it turned out, at some point during a certain class, the teacher changed the project from being just a flyer to a catalog, involving intensive research and Internet-cited sources. I say "at some point" because I missed that point in class where the rules of the game were changed. All my life I had been told that you couldn't change the rules of the game once it had started, but here I am. I dunno…maybe my Spanish teacher isn't familiar with this American custom.

Once the teacher returned my pitiful poster, now graded, it was perfectly clear what she thought of it. The following was inked on the backside: "No websites, No sizes, No prices, No description, No pictures of items, (Resulting Grade) 50." I wanted to say that it wasn't my fault, but I didn't know how to word that in Spanish, and Sean didn't know either.

I hate most of the Spanish projects because the lot of them are reincarnations of the kinds of projects that were assigned to us in sixth grade. Y'know, the ones that were big on pretty colors and paper cutouts. Here I am again, years later, still trying to beg for a few extra points because I colored inside the lines. The only thing that we've ever done that was of any value in Spanish class was our video project. We knew what we were doing on that. Everything came together for this ten-minute cooking show that Mikey, Serena, and yours truly pulled off. It was risible to me, but most of the really funny jokes went unnoticed because it was, of course, entirely in Spanish. That's the overall theme of Spanish projects—your greatest achievements belittled and disparaged to their smallest possible denomination.

We are in the process of watching *Babe*, and no matter how stupid you thought the idea of a talking pig becoming a sheep dog was in English, it's a hell of a lot worse in Spanish. Sure, you'll get a cheap laugh when you hear the duck ramble out several lines in gibberish in a voice that sounds like Gilbert Gottfried with the flu, but most of it is less than what you would call amusing. We have to answer questions (given to us in Spanish) while watching it, which just kills the mood. We all wind up failing them, and what better way to learn than by failing miserably? It's not like we can understand anything of what is being said. When you learn the words in a textbook, they come off as being nice and simple. But people who speak Spanish don't speak the language like it's written. People who speak Spanish tend to promenade through sentences as fast as they can breathe without hyperventilating. You know how us native English-speaking people have spaces in between words? Spanish people chatter like there aren't any spaces. It's all just one line, and they spit it out without thinking twice of inhaling sweet, sweet oxygen.

Nothing shows our lack of understanding of the Spanish language more than when we are about to take tests or quizzes. They tend to sneak up on us. They always do. No one ever knows about tests or quizzes beforehand. Ever. Chances are that you'll find out about one during the day appointed for it from that one smart kid who was paying attention (Buddha knows why). You'll frantically ready yourself for it, prepare your cheat sheets (convenience sheets), and learn every fact made available in the last two weeks in just under two minutes. Most of us are studying as soon as we show up for class. Some might say we do it for the adrenaline rush, but I say that we're just stupid when it comes to these things. You'll never see a more dejected face on kids than right after they take a Spanish test. They all slump in their desks, make the hand signal for shooting themselves in the head, and wear expressions along the lines of, "Why have we been forsaken?"

As bad as all of this is, it's not nearly as bad as when Pom isn't there. In most classes, we would gladly rejoice at having a substitute. In here, however, having a substitute means that the system will be resorting to using her back-up lesson plan, which always, *always* involves translating large quantities of valueless Spanish text into English. Even this wouldn't be so bad, since we had Sean among us to make sense of it all. But then, the unthinkable happened. The subs started to *forbid* the use of any cooperative learning among us. Dammit! No one was hit harder than Josh, who has been relying on this cooperative learning process for quite some time now. "I'm supposed to translate this on my own?!" he asked, in a bout of fury. "That will take *days*! Do you have any idea how long that is?!" Umm, she might, Josh. She just might.

He was in for an even bigger surprise when he got it back, corrected. "What?! I was thinking of the right answer! Why did I put this down?!"

I tried to force some optimism to console him, but it didn't go over too well. "Josh, look at it as a learning experience."

I don't know how anyone rephrases "failure" into "learning experience." I don't think he does either. "Yeah, or a learning disability!" he countered.

During the last five or ten minutes of class on good days, we'll play a little game. Everyone pulls his or her desk into a circle that wraps around the classroom, with Pom's desk being the cornerstone at the front. She takes out a tennis ball and bounce-passes it to one of the kids in the circle. Whoever catches the ball has to tell what a Spanish word that she gives means in English. Once you answer it, you throw the ball to someone else. After five minutes, I came to one and only one deduction: We suck at this game. Not because we don't know Spanish, but because our eye-hand coordination is horrendous. We can't catch and we can't throw to save our lives. The ball bounces too soon or too late, and the kid at the other end doesn't even see it coming. It's thrown too hard, a few get nailed in the face (Serena, of all people, being the first), and it rolls around on the floor while the others kick it. When it finally rolls to a stop in the middle of the circle, the desks are packed too closely together for us to get up and get it. We suck at this.

Already there has been a lot of talk of taking French next year for a language credit. I'll stick with Spanish for one more year because I'm stupid like that. I'll also go through this one more class like I'm on death row, waiting for a word from the governor (a.k.a. the bell to ring), quietly laughing to myself as I imagine what would happen if that tennis ball were to suddenly burst into flames. We're all asking ourselves the same question right about now. That of, "What the hell was I thinking when I was filling out that course selection sheet last year?" This class is bullshit. They're all bullshit. We're shifting through each day looking for some meaning to it all. We're waking up each day thinking that today will be new and wonderful in some way or form, and going to sleep each night disappointed. Fuck this place. Two more years and I'm gone for good.

Then, all at once, someone targets me with the tennis ball. I'm not in the mood to answer any more Spanish stuff, so I sit perfectly still and hope that there's topspin on it that will send it to somebody else. Nope, it's coming right at me...and clips me in the neck. Not the best place to be struck, but there are worse places. Trust me, I've been hit there plenty of times with plenty of balls (no pun intended). Pom is angered at my lack of participation, and is about to say something when

RIIIIIIIIINNNNNNNNNNGGGGGGGGGGGGGGGGG!!!

I shout out, "¡Gracias!" then bounce the ball to her and walk out, the words still hanging on the tip of her tongue.

Miscellaneous Philosophy—Part 8
Too Many Opinions for My Own Good

This is what I believe we should do in order to solve the problem of underfunded schools: Every time a city/town/village cuts the school budget, all the students of that area should riot and burn stuff. In a few years, we'd either have the best schools or the best police force in the world. So it's a win-win situation.

Do your kids a favor—don't reproduce.

I was walking down the halls one day, and a student came up to me asked, very politely, if I wanted to make a donation to FBLA. And I said to her, You're asking me if I want to make a donation to the Future Business Leaders of America? Let's take a moment to think about this one: If the future BUSINESS leaders of America need money, shouldn't they do some BUSINESS and get some?

"...do some business and get some..." that didn't sound right at all.

Honestly, what kind of idiot types up a report and then lists sparknotes.com on his work-cited page?

As an appeal to writers and advertisers everywhere, I would like you to stop using take-offs of the Ten Commandments. They're not cute, they're not funny, and they're sure as hell not innovative or creative by any means. Just stop. I don't need the *Ten Commandments of Arithmetic* telling me "Thou shall not divide by zero."

Words of Wisdom: Don't ever get into an argument about the environment. Chances are you'll start off with the words "ecology and conservation," and every time you do that, you run the risk of inadvertently saying "ecology and conversation." And as soon as you've done that, you're screwed. You've already lost the argument.

Every now and then, your blood comes to a boiling point, and you gather the nerve and the anger to ask an unsuspecting teacher, "How is this ever going to help me in life?" And every now and then, some of them get the bright idea to use a snappy comeback along the lines of, "It's a good thing to know if you're ever on *Jeopardy!*" Well, if I'm on *Jeopardy*, then high school didn't prepare me for life too well, now did it?

The AFTER Chapter

Free at last. Free at last! Thank God Almighty we are free at last! Everyone is slightly happier about the end of the day, and we are certainly grateful that it's the end of the day, but no one really shows any enthusiasm. We go about the halls and to our lockers like we are about to get ready for the next class, except now we're getting our coats, and we're walking straight past every classroom. And we're walking a little bit faster. Or at least, I am. I ain't hangin' around here any more than I have to. You have to be careful about exiting. If you try to run, you'll be an instant target for verbal abuse, as that's what the retarded kids do…I'm sorry, what the "special" kids do. As it is I get made fun of because I go down stairs slightly faster than most. I can't help it. It must be the shoes or something.

There's a decent amount of people who are staying after for whatever reason—detention students, sports participants, a few others who have club organization obligations. I'd try to persecute the ones on their way to their Amnesty International meetings, but most of them are Goths, and Goths scare the shit out of me. If it were the fall season, I'd be staying until around 5:30 p.m. for volleyball practice, or even later if it was a game day. That sport has given me a lot of memories, and I think at least a few of them are good. I've stayed after for the school's television production club before, but Buddha knows why. I met some good people while I was there, but they've all long since graduated. A few months later than this time last year, I was attending track practice. I don't really want to get back into my feelings about that.

I never joined any clubs for a lot of reasons. Even though I rarely have anything to do in my spare time, that fact never brought me to the conclusion that I had to join some kind of club. I don't like to make indefinite time commitments. But mostly it was because I didn't trust people. Knowing what I know now

175

about all the kids in this school, I don't see how I could. What would I join? I can already rule out both Amnesty International and the Future Business Leaders of America right off the bat. I don't trust their motives. The nonsensical left wing socialist circle filled with Bolsheviks in hiding and a group of carnivorous capitalists who have trouble understanding the meaning of capitalism—I don't trust those bastards one bit.

The Youth and Government Club? That's stupid. They don't allow youth in government, and there's a reason for that. Student Council? What the hell do those guys do? I've asked members before, and no one has given me a straight answer. I think that they should vote to disband themselves—no one would see that coming (except for me, of course). I ran for class president during my freshman year. No big deal—I was self-nominated. I lost, but only because it was rigged in favor of Jen. They made us revote for that thing at least three times. It screamed "suspicious," if you ask me. I don't question democracy, but I do question the bureaucratic oligarchy. Damn oligarchies.

What about the Fellowship of Christian Athletes? I didn't even know there was such a thing as the Fellowship of Christian Athletes up until a few months ago. It sounds like a much more relaxed version of the Knights of Columbus. I don't trust the Knights of Columbus, either. But don't tell anyone I said that! The KoC has spies everywhere. I don't trust them at all. Them and PETA.

I'm perfectly fine with going home at the appointed time every day. I don't see anything wrong with that, though I am a little concerned about the kids who feel the need to live and breathe school life for as long as possible. You know, the ones who are involved in *everything*? That's when I'm glad that we employ a full-time social worker. The system keeps asking me the same question, over and over again: "How are you going to get into college without any extracurricular activities?" I hate that word "extracurricular." It's far too big and it's used far too often. I've made it a point to not fall into that trap. School should be a function of your life, not the other way around.

I walk down the stairs, down the last stretch of hallway, and out the main entrance. It's a glorious feeling to make this final expedition, this one last leg of the journey. I can't wait until the last day of school. Then it goes from glorious to euphoric. The main entrance is the exiting gateway of choice for most of us. A few go out a stairwell exit on the other end of the school—whichever way is faster. A few go down the fire exits. I raced Mike down one of those once. He won, but I was a close second. The rules about going up the UP stairs and down the DOWN stairs are suspended at the end of the day for convenience. Yeah, I never thought that common sense would play a part in this myself.

When you're a freshman, every day is a new adventure. For some, I think it still is. But I remember a day when I was a freshman and walking down the last major hallway to the exit doors. It was a few weeks before prom, and the Students Against Destructive Decisions (S.A.D.D.) organization was having a special activity to remind kids not to drive drunk on prom night. Every period during that day, several members of S.A.D.D. would "die," change into black clothing, and stop talking for the rest of the day in order to represent kids killed on prom night due to drunk driving (that whole "one in seven kids"-type analogy). At the end of the day, all the "dead" members (about twenty or thirty kids) lined up side-by-side along the last part of the hallway that I am meandering down.

The thing was, during my freshman year I was not aware that S.A.D.D. had created this special activity. I was, in fact, not aware of the existence of S.A.D.D. itself. Here I was, then, walking down this stretch of corridor, with thirty kids dressed in black staring at me, not a word being spoken between them. I could hear a soft bell ringing in the background, but I couldn't tell where it was coming from. And for the life of me, I couldn't figure out what the hell was going on. I walked outside, shuddered, and asked myself (and later, others), "What was *that*?"

At first, I thought it was an elaborate senior prank. Or maybe it was a part of *Trigger Happy TV*, looking for one of the disguised participants to be Dom Jolly. Or perhaps this was some kind of practical joke, and at any moment Ashton Kutcher would pop out of the bushes and inform me that I had been thoroughly punk'd. No such luck. I didn't find out what it was all about until several weeks later. In the meantime, I suffered a series of sporadic nightmares.

I have mixed feelings about S.A.D.D.'s idea of a warped public service announcement. Sure, it's important to prevent kids from driving drunk (or anyone, for that matter). But did *all* the members *have* to die of drunk driving *on prom night*? That just lacks creativity. Why not have kids die of other destructive decisions? Then I would join! I would want to be the guy who trips on LSD and stands in front of a train in order to try to stop it because the drugs have distorted my sense of reality. Not only would it be fun, but it would also send a very important message to today's kids: It's classic to stay off acid!...Folks, it's the best I could come up with on such short notice.

Well, that story didn't really have any relevance. It was just a strange happening that took place along this last stretch of hallway. Best not to dwell on old memories, I suppose. Out and away I go. After the last set of doors, there's about fifty feet of sidewalk to trudge down. It's not all that cold out. The afternoons around this time of year tend to thaw a little as the temperature hovers around thirty-five, forty degrees. It gives the outdoors a muggy, wet, disgusting feel, almost as if you can taste the moisture in the air and feel the grimy slush on the bottom of your shoes. A light snowfall drifts down from a clear blue sky. It's borderline surreal, but no one bothers to notice. No one but me.

The Bus Ride Home

Whenever I prepare for a journey, I prepare as though for death.
Should I never return, all is in order.
—Katherine Mansfield

I walk onto a nearly empty bus, with the only one on being Tom. He's sitting way in the back, the last seat on the right side, the same place where he always sits. He always gets here before everyone else, but the rest of us have yet to figure out how. The heater is blasting enough hot air to fill a small blimp, and the windows are steaming. It's like a sauna in here. I take my seat, way in the back, the last seat on the left side, the same place where I always sit. We'll trade jokes about how bad all of our classes were today. It's nothing new—they're always bad/boring/laborious/ whatever.

Soon after my arrival, Mike comes on. He takes his seat way in the back on the right side, right in front of Tom, like he always does. Mike, a kid who is normally overflowing with sprightliness and (from what I've seen him do in gym class) a nearly endless reserve of vim and vigor, seems depleted at the end of the day. He's not running, he's not laughing, he's not smiling—he's barely talking. Mike's anger is usually infused with his sense of humor, which helps him deal with it all, I guess. Now, though, he speaks very plainly of what's bothering him. His complaints don't often deviate from the norm of people, classes, etc. Get him into a conversation, and he won't mind displaying his despair verbally. Hey, Mike! Did you hear about (random student idiocy)?

"...That's so stupid. If I had a girlfriend, *which I never will...*"

It's odd, because I know several girls who think he's hot stuff. Maybe he does, too. Maybe he doesn't care.

Soon after my arrival, Dan comes on. Dan is rarely ever on the bus. Most of the time, he'll come on, stay for several minutes (if that), and then leave. Sometimes, he stays. Other times, he doesn't. There's no obvious pattern to the days that he stays and the days that he leaves, and none of us have ever thought to question him about it. That's Dan, and that's that. And away he goes, giving us a short farewell on his way out, if that's what you want to call it.

Once Tom, Mike, and myself are firmly established in our chosen—some might say destined—seats, Anna arrives. It seems that I haven't yet gone into a particularized synopsis of Anna. And I shall, because she's a subject worth expounding on (and because I fear for my life if I don't).

And Now, a Little Something about Anna (Because I'm Sure She's Anticipating This)

Trust everybody, but cut the cards.
                                        —*Finley Peter Dunne*

I'm not sure how I first met Anna. She's not really sure how she first met me. Nonetheless, we met (somehow), and now she's on my bus. In the morning, she sits with Mike, but in the afternoon she sits with me. I don't think there are any guys who would object to having to sit with her. She's a bit taller than the average girl, and, it has to be said, a little prettier than the average girl. Her long brown hair—on some days straight but curled on others—comes halfway down her back. Her clothes are always fashionable, and somehow, *somehow*, she manages to look sexy no matter what she's wearing. Thin, but not to the point of being too thin, muscles finely toned, but not to the point that it would make you feel uneasy (or inadequate). A complexion ever so fair, a smile that can melt you, eyes that can seduce you—hook, line, and sinker.

Having pointed out all the nice things about her, it's only sporting that I point out the rest. We can make some apologies and some excuses because she's a freshman, but not enough to be completely justifiable. She has a strong sense of morals and ethics, but at the same time, she's unbelievably shallow. Looks are important, having a car is important, and being an upperclassman is required before you even make the list of possible boyfriends. And that list seems to grow with each passing day. She's beautiful, and she knows it. And if you don't know it, she'll promptly inform you of it. She knows that she looks good; she knows that you want her; she knows that she can rip you to pieces if she so desires. She's not self-absorbed, but believe me, *she knows*.

She'll openly acknowledge that the time she's spending in high school is, so far, the best years of her life (despite having not completed a full year yet). So you can imagine how hard it is for someone like me, just getting over several serious depressive episodes, to be happy for her. She keeps telling everyone else younger than her that they're going to love, and I mean absolutely *love*, high school. It really pisses me off sometimes. Okay, all the time. I just don't want her to give anyone false expectations. It's not fun for everyone. I'm sure I could find some kids who would agree with me wholeheartedly.

For every good quality that she possesses, there's a really glaringly offensive quality that counters it. For every favorable, pleasurable feeling that she can give you to warm your heart, she has a gut-wrenching, displeasing sentiment that can stick in the pit of your stomach. Maybe I'm partly responsible. Some of my sarcastic ways are becoming part of her character. All of this leaves me with only one thing to say: I don't get it. I've looked over every aspect of her personality, and I simply don't get it. I give up. She has a mixture, a potency even, that defies description. I've stopped making any effort to figure her out, because I get these massive headaches every time I try.

She walks down the aisle of the bus, on some days with a broad smile and on others with small grin. Today, it's something in the middle. She takes her seat way in the back on the left side with me, like she always does. She slouches down, curling her long, silky-smooth legs in front of her, knees resting firmly against the back of the seat in front of us. I do the same, even though I don't really have the "silky smooth" part to match. "Hi," she says, her voice clear, clean, crisp, fluent...graceful. The name "Anna" means "gracious," after all.

"Hey," is my only response. We're not really big on salutations anymore. I'm not sure if we ever were. Most kids I know aren't. Casual parley between the four of us ensues at a moderate pace, with Anna asking Mike how things are going with Jen, me tactfully reminding her that Jen has a boyfriend. "Yeah, but she could do so much better than him." Don't say anything, Stefan. Don't say anything. That will only make things worse.

The bus pulls out of the high school driveway, along with a dozen others. It turns left, and makes its way down the street to the middle school to pick up an excessive amount of kids, Kevin being one of the many. Kevin is in eighth grade and a friend of Mike's. Anna has been giving him advice about high school throughout the year (most of it bullshit), and he's been telling us not to expect much from next year's freshmen. Just as we predicted. The back six seats (three on either side) are strictly reserved for kids in high school. This is a good thing, because it means that each of us pretty much gets our own seat. The middle school kids, by contrast, who outnumber us three to one (at least), are crammed into the remaining seats. Yes, that's it. Laugh. Laugh at their suffering! We're not required to care. That's the best part about being in high school—not being required to care. Sympathy is not a prerequisite to acceptance. Not in our high school, at any rate, no matter how racist, homophobic, or down-right cruel the subject may be. That's right, "prerequisite." Thank you, Word of the Day Calendar!

The bus ride home is probably the best part of my day. Wait— not probably, definitely. All of us can let go of every tension, and say whatever we want. It's not that we were really afraid of being judged before, or that we won't get judged now, but most things can be forgiven as part of the post-drama world of intermission from unfeigned realness. We fall into some pretty unusual con-versations that sidetrack from ordinary. This was where I first got the idea to write a book. It was the end result of an argument with Tom about something (but about what escapes me at the moment). I told him, "I will prove you wrong, Tom! I'll take all of my crazy and wildly inaccurate ravings and put them into a book! And I'll call it…" And then, in an instant, it came to me: "Miscellaneous Philosophy!"

"That title doesn't make any sense!" he asseverated.

"Of course it doesn't, Tom!" I retorted. "It's not supposed to!" I guess I showed him who's boss, right? Nah, he'll still argue about it, even though it's not likely that he remembers what we were arguing about either. I even doubt that he remembers any part of that exchange. Tom had some interesting concepts of his own. The most revolutionary of these being...

THE Theorem

A word to the wise ain't necessary.
It's the stupid ones that need the advice.

— Bill Cosby

In short, what it does is prove his nonexistence in the molecular universe, which I found quite interesting (if not annoying). It's just like Tom to come up with something like this. He doesn't feel pain, he doesn't feel the cold, he doesn't talk. I mean, he'll talk to me on the bus, and he'll talk to Mike, but hardly ever to anyone else anywhere else. Anna? No, he never talks to her, no matter what. It's just how he operates. It's just like him to come up with a theorem of how he's not responsible for anything.

If you find that the idea of nonexistence in the molecular universe is way over your head, you can just skip the next few paragraphs. However, the concept of it is not too difficult to comprehend, so I think it's worth giving a shot. First off, recall the saying, "I think, therefore I am." Now assume the opposite of the statement. If he doesn't think, then he doesn't exist. In all good reason, you could ask, "How does one not think?" My answer, or perhaps his answer, is that it doesn't necessarily imply thinking—it could also assume the form of ignorance, apathy, and lethargy. In other words: I don't know, I don't care, I don't do, and therefore I am not.

To best understand this, assume Tom's existence not in a physical sense, but in a mathematical sense: the number 0 (zero). Zero at its center (of meaning, not existence) implies nothing. By nature, it implies the absence of anything. Now, I can assure you that Tom is still very much visible in our world. So is the number zero. You can see it and write it (or in Tom's case, talk to it) however much you want, but it is still, nonetheless, nothing. This does not imply that it does not witness everything around it or that it does not cause anything, as in the case of hear no evil, see no evil, speak no evil. Not in the least bit. Tom, like the number zero, still affects the other people (numbers) around him, and Tom causes havoc just like anything else. (Who hasn't dealt with an equation in which the presence of zero makes things incredibly more complicated?) Since he is nothing, though, he doesn't feel any rebound of the effects he causes, which is to be expected.

Now you might ask (if any of this makes any sense to you), "But how can he still perform tasks like walking or writing or doing homework if he doesn't exist?" Once again, the answer is mathematical. You can add or subtract zero from anything and get a result. It is still the same number, naturally, because it is nothing; although the numbers (or people) are affected by this equation (situation), or else there wouldn't be an equation. Unfortunately, mathematics does not currently possess a method for describing this effect, which might be fathomable considering that humans aren't numbers even though they can be described by such (much in the same way that letters make up our name and describe us, even though we aren't physically a language). Basically he's there, but he doesn't exist.

Which is just as well, because when he is here, he generally pisses people off with his theorems of nonexistence. You have to know how to pick your battles, and this was one that I just let him have. He wasn't the only one who would throw us off with zany rigmarole, either.

Sixteen Years in the Life

Adults, having repressed their own painful memories, often describe the teenage years as "the best years of your life." But teenagers know firsthand the worry, cruelty, and competition; the pressures and responsibilities; the fears and confusions; the humiliations and torments; the jealousies and rivalries.
    —*Excerpted from* How Rude! The Teenagers' Guide To Good Manners, Proper Behavior, and Not Grossing People Out, *by Alex J. Packer, PhD, ©1997. Used with permission from Free Spirit Publishing, Inc.*

Anna, by nature, is very…unique, in a lot of regards (as am I, if you haven't already guessed). But there are a few things that still stand out in my mind. I have to point out—even though she most likely doesn't want me to—that she spent the early part of her high school career smoking a lot of marijuana (weed, in layman's terms). She says that she's quit since then, but every now and then, you get the inkling that the damage has already been done.

One day on the bus, for example, Kevin wanted to show us the T-shirt that he had underneath his basketball jersey. So he lifts the jersey up over his head, but not quite high enough so that we can read whatever it is that's written on his T-shirt. A short while later, he realizes this, and Anna and I discover why we've been staring at Kevin's back for the last five minutes.

Kevin and I gave a light chuckle at this unexpected circumstance, as you might have done had you been there. Anna, however, laughed so much you'd think Jerry Seinfeld accidentally regurgitated his lunchtime Mexican chili on a midget or something. I tell you now—and it is by no means an exaggeration—she laughed for ten minutes straight. I found myself getting a little worried, since she was laughing so hard that she was having a great amount of difficulty breathing, and was starting to hyperventilate. That's how she was for the rest of the bus ride. When she got off at her stop, she was still laughing. Two weeks later, while she was sitting in her seat, she started laughing for no apparent reason. It was the same situation from two weeks prior that was tickling her sense of humor. Sometimes, it makes you wonder.

But as long as she's within earshot, all we're allowed to do is wonder. Her first months as a freshman are something that she professes to be not one of her proudest moments. My psychological axioms on freshman behavior aren't something that I've pulled out of thin air. I've seen them in action—more than once, I'm afraid. I remember Anna during the early part of her freshman year. She loved every minute of it. But soon after her life as a high school student commenced, she fell into a bad crowd, as it were, a not-so-sound group of kids. Tom, Mike, and myself...we all knew that these kids were not the best of people to associate with, to put it lightly. She didn't know it at the time. She thought they were the greatest thing to ever happen to her. The rest of us were concerned, but we didn't say anything. I think we reasoned that she wouldn't believe us even if we had told her the truth, and that she would figure it out on her own eventually. It bothers me now and then...the fact that I never said anything. She doesn't hold it against any of us, but in the depths of my conscience...sometimes ...

Eventually, she became more and more aware of what was going on. Everything started becoming painfully evident that things were not as they seemed. Her world, as she knew it (and you may think I'm being melodramatic when I say this, but I really don't think I am), began to collapse all around her. She spent many bus rides home telling us about every detrimental thing that was happening. You could see it in her eyes, I swear. You could see that she was completely disillusioned about everything that was taking place. It took several angry conversations back and forth with her so-called friends and at least one violent hallway encounter before she came to her senses.

We were right. She had figured it out on her own, but it was a hollow victory. She stopped hanging out with those kids, quit smoking, and turned everything around. A success story? I guess you could label it as that. But every once in a while, there's an awkward moment of silence or two. "Stefan," she asked me at one point whilst discussing the days of her brief brush with drugs, "do you think less of me as a person because of what I've done?" I still haven't answered that question. Not to her, not to myself—not to anyone.

Mike doesn't care for melodrama. He shouts out his window at the kids walking down the sidewalk, trying to see how many of them he can get to look up at him. He makes a note of how many do, how many yell back at him, and how many give him the finger. Immature? No, never. Mike tries to enjoy life at face value, and that's a quality that should be treasured, not spurned.

While Mike is reveling in his self-induced amusement, Anna has a few good stories to tell. I'm not even sure if she knows what it's like to have a boring day. She'll talk with few breaks in the waterfall of words, stopping only to enjoy her favorite song. Every song is her favorite song. *Every single one.* The bus radio blares over the cheap speakers, treating music like harmony was an expletive. Perhaps the song is some kind of love song by Maroon 5, a band whose name directly spells out its members: five guys who should have been marooned on a deserted island far, far away, a long, long time ago. Or maybe it's none other than Britney Spears, spewing her toxic waste all over the radio waves.

There is no more radio. There's a playlist of five songs, played over and again, their order rarely changing. I've heard the same songs played on the bus in and on the bus out, day in and day out, for weeks on end. Radio DJs, who have been given way more power than they should have ever been allotted, ramble through the first thirty seconds of the song, and then through the last thirty seconds of the song, thinking all the while that they have something important to say. Normally, I wouldn't complain—I'd just turn it off. But being on the bus, I can't. I am forced to endure it, day in, day out, day in, day out…

Here we all are then, sharing in a bizarre bonding moment of sorts, the only similarity that we all share being that we're on this one particular bus, all of us synchronously on a daily basis for a good three or four years now. We share memories of all varieties—like that time Mike fit a rubber glove over his entire head and managed to inflate it to three times its original size. Or that time Mike and Tom were trying to kill each other. Or that time that I tried to break a window with Mike's head (and almost succeeded). Or one of those rare incidents in which Anna and I had one of our intensely bitter arguments. We've come to an agreement—I get to make jokes about teen pregnancy, and she gets to make jokes about rape. Fair is fair.

The nexus achieved on the bus ride home is something that can only truly be cherished during your underclassman years. After all, this is the last year, the last months even, that we'll all be on the bus together. After this, who knows what? We'll probably just drift apart, the logical end, slow and painful. I'd like to end this paragraph with a dramatic image, so if you could just picture me with a single tear rolling down the side of my cheek, I'd be much obliged.

The bus comes to that same four-way intersection that we visited a mere seven hours earlier. Anna and Kevin bid us "later" and walk off. From here, the route goes straight down a hill, only to turn around once it reaches the bottom. That damned beeping sound that large vehicles make whenever they back up has been collectively decided as the most annoying sound ever created by a machine. We head back up the hill we just came down, and then drive down a few more streets to get to Mike's stop. He gets off without saying a word on most days. Maybe there's a mutual understanding somewhere in the stillness of the moment. Maybe we're just nervous about final good-byes.

In a few minutes, I'll be getting off, as well. Tom is the last one off the bus every day, but I've never heard him complain about it. It feels kind of infelicitous to be along this stretch of road that leads up to my stop. Here I am at sixteen. I've been riding this same bus route for one hundred and eighty days annually since kindergarten. Soon it will all be a thing of the past, an old memento of the psyche, and, years later, a frequent topic of discussion with my psychologist as he documents yet another case of a mid-life crisis.

I look out the glass at the same sights that have hardly changed in more than a decade. Several snowflakes drift in from an open window a few seats in front of me. The distance between here and my final destination steadily shrinks by the second. I know what you're thinking. You're thinking that this is the happy ending, right? This is where I leave off on the after chapter, with some quintessential statement like, "And now I see that these were the best days of my life." Why wouldn't you think that? I've given all the standard outlines for such a finish. Sometimes I like to think that it's the happy ending I'm looking for myself. I mean, it has all the elements for the perfect wrap-up. Think about all these people: Brianna, Mike, Josh, Serena, Mikey, Kate, Anna, Tom, Kevin, Luke, Neil, John, Sean, Joe…It's the perfect group of friends, isn't it?

As it turns out, it's not. The whole thing is a phantasm that we've been putting faith into since day one. Most of those kids fiercely hate each other. Dark truths and black facts that we've been afraid to own up to…the idea that this whole concept of reality is just a nightmare with intermittent periods of waking up in cold sweats before going back into the dreary sleep. I've discovered a lot about high school in these past two years. There's nothing magical about it, or special, or even worthwhile. It's merely a place. A moment in time. Odd feelings, unnecessary embarrassment, and a last-ditch, lackluster performance by childhood.

So here I am among all these kids, brought together by an inadvertent spasm on the part of Fate. I'm the only common connection to all of them. And who am I? I'm just some kid who's made their acquaintanceship. An undistinguished anomaly who's trying to pass through the muck of the world amongst every bane of existence, and letting go of so much in the process. At the end of everything, I just feel...lost. Very lost.

The bus approaches my driveway and lets me off, my journey completed for today.

About the AUTHOR

Stefan Koski grew up in the small town of Terryville, Connecticut. He spent most of his time during his underclassman years attempting to adapt to the high school lifestyle (without much success). His dark witticism and sarcastic personality were constant companions during the unhealthy period of adjustment, and his longtime efforts to justify his own aberrations and insecurities can be seen throughout his first book (this one), which was written and published when he was sixteen.

Although a skilled writer, he hopes to develop his talents for film and to one day write and direct his own movies.

Printed in the United States
38763LVS00004B/277